GIANT PENCIL PASTIMES®

BOOK OF CROSSWORDS

RICHARD MANCHESTER

BRISTOL
PARK
BOOKS

Bristol Park Books
252 W. 38th Street
NYC, NY 10018

Bristol Park Books is a registered trademark of
Bristol Park Books, Inc.

Pencil Pastimes ® is a registered trademark of Bristol
Park Books, Inc.

Published by arrangement with Crosstown Publications

ISBN: 978-0-88486-510-0

Printed in the United States of America

Contents

Puzzles 1

Answers 230

Puzzles

1

EASY

ACROSS

1. Animal companion
4. Practice boxing
8. In addition
12. Actress Gardner
13. Arrive at O'Hare
14. Homeowner's document
15. Tear (apart)
16. Ancient
17. Cherished
18. Votes into office
20. Challenge
21. While
22. Irrigated
25. Grouch
28. Husbands, to wives
29. Behold!
30. Boy
31. More ashen in color
32. Donkey
33. By
34. Travels via ship
35. Run from capture
36. Writing aids
38. Laugh sound
39. Makes a mistake
40. Package
44. Talks wildly
46. Derby or bonnet
47. Wide street: abbr.
48. Vicinity
49. Rational
50. Ball-point item
51. Microbe
52. Lyric poems
53. Historical age

DOWN

1. Use a peeling gadget
2. Sinful
3. Record on cassette
4. Mail-chute openings
5. Buddies
6. Plus
7. Travel route: abbr.
8. Worships
9. Prying bar
10. Use the eyes
11. Strange
17. Afterward
19. Taxi
20. Goes out with socially
22. Room dividers
23. Otherwise
24. Medicinal amount
25. Applaud
26. Fixed price
27. Paid notice
28. Posts (a letter)
31. Couples
32. Actor Pacino
34. Shriek
35. Distant
37. No way!
38. Detests
40. Window glass
41. — Cod, Mass.
42. Always
43. Songstress Horne
44. Cloth for dusting
45. "We — the World"
46. Owned
49. Thus

1

2

ACROSS

1. Taxi
4. Be defeated
8. Smoke thread
12. In the manner of: 2 wds.
13. Norse god
14. Diva's solo
15. Colorful Arizona plateau: 2 wds.
18. Nose
19. Square-dance grouping
20. Northwestern Italian city
23. Prepared
27. Poet Lazarus
30. Against
32. Government espionage group: abbr.
33. Annoyance: 4 wds. (slang)
36. Under the weather
37. Sleuth Wolfe
38. "Beware, the — of March"
39. Prison units
41. The one and only: abbr.
43. Affirmative vote
45. Ms. Rivera
49. Goes out on a spree: 3 wds. (slang)
54. Snake, e.g.
55. Equal
56. Soft metal
57. Ms. Horne
58. Snead and Houston
59. Moslem title

DOWN

1. Berets
2. Mr. Arkin
3. Actor, Scott —
4. Bingolike game
5. Lyric poem
6. Comic Caesar
7. Concludes
8. Fritter away
9. Anger
10. Knight's title
11. Butter square
16. Pitcher Ryan
17. Weird
21. Scandinavian
22. Opening song, for short
24. Served perfectly
25. Casino cubes
26. "Chews the fat": slang
27. Lengthy tale
28. Boy or man
29. Grinding machine
31. Son of 13-Across
34. Map feature
35. Darkness
40. Actress Carter
42. Freezers
44. Cleopatra's snakes
46. Greek letter
47. Small branch
48. Ballerina Pavlova
49. Chum
50. King Kong, e.g.
51. Charged atom
52. Pekoe or oolong
53. Skirt edge

ACROSS

1. Vitality
4. Seize
8. Common seasoning
12. Eugene's State: abbr.
13. Speed contest
14. Threesome
15. Participate (in)
17. New Orleans athlete
18. Fruit drink
19. Buccaneer
20. Vine fruit
23. Simple
24. Solitary
25. Peel
26. Poisonous snake
29. Opposed (to)
31. Stir up
33. Lawn moisture
34. Bucket
36. Aroma
37. Bovine baby
38. Used a broom
39. Prying bars
42. That woman
43. Wear away
44. Hire, as an airplane
48. Location
49. Passage
50. Grow older
51. Perceives
52. Heavy cord
53. Supreme Being

DOWN

1. Soft drink
2. Epoch
3. For each
4. Mark, as test papers
5. Lawn tool
6. Expert
7. Exist
8. Look fixedly (at)
9. Prima donna's solo
10. Cloth ravelings
11. Carry
16. Long, slender candle
17. Warning signal
19. Danger
20. Happy
21. Roam
22. Once again
23. Pa's mate
25. Chimes
26. Assistant
27. Cease
28. Saucy
30. Extra
32. Cringe
35. In case that
37. Relinquishes
38. Portion
39. Not as many
40. A Great Lake
41. Cast a ballot
42. Go marketing
44. Cote sound
45. Playground game
46. Conceit
47. Scarlet
49. Physician: abbr.

MEDIUM

ACROSS

1. Marble
6. Feline
9. Taxi
12. Ms. Streep
13. Be indebted
14. Fib
15. Cent
16. Portable light
18. That is: abbr.
19. Ms. MacGraw
20. Sunbeams
21. Dined
23. Maker of sweaters
25. Myself
26. Sound quality
27. Helps commit a crime
30. Whole
32. Fungus variety
33. Theater part
34. Lacking color
35. Scale note
36. Guides
38. Shade tree
39. Mimic
41. Raw mineral
42. Singer Jarreau
43. Deletes unacceptable material, as from a movie
45. Change
48. Bonnet, for one
49. — Grande
50. Cooking appliance
51. Overhead trains
52. Competed in a race
53. Sharpened

DOWN

1. Electrical unit, for short
2. Golly!
3. Golfer Palmer, to friends
4. Actress Daly
5. Former "Tarzan," Ron —
6. Lassie was one
7. Anticipate
8. Decade number
9. — out, departed
10. Well-ventilated
11. Gazzara and Vereen
17. Triple
19. Singer Murray
21. Iowa town
22. Canvas shelter
23. M*A*S*H locale
24. Follows, detective-style: slang
26. Detroit team
28. Inform
29. Did the "crawl"
31. Natural skills
32. Female horse
34. Human being
37. Andrea —, ocean liner
38. Singer John
39. Dull pain
40. Loud ringing of bells
42. Choir voice
44. Famous hockey name
45. Fire residue
46. Actress Arden
47. Crimson

MEDIUM

ACROSS

1. Young child
4. Massachusetts city
9. High card
12. Corn spike
13. Fragrance
14. Sheep's cry
15. Dined
16. Small piece
17. "Guys and —"
19. Require
21. Peppy
22. Change
24. Stockings
25. "— Hand Luke"
26. Buffalo
27. In the direction of
29. Move swiftly
30. Burdened
31. Attorney's concern
32. Newspaper VIP: abbr.
33. More sensible
34. Like a skyscraper
35. Picnic pests
36. Money depositories
37. Peek
40. Drinking vessels
41. Western show
42. 2000 pounds
43. Mischievous child
46. Also
47. Gain knowledge
49. And not
50. Affirmative reply
51. British nursemaid
52. Sticky stuff: slang

DOWN

1. Afternoon beverage
2. Cereal grain
3. New Jersey capital
4. Cavalry sword
5. Dry
6. Parking —
7. Dorothy's Auntie
8. Dolley or James
9. Adept
10. Shout
11. Simple
18. Baking chamber
20. Snakelike fish
21. Defeated one
22. Land measure
23. Noisy
24. Conceals
26. Moisten while roasting
27. Chat
28. Night birds
30. 16th U.S. President
31. Michigan capital
33. Decrease
34. Faucet
36. Rabbit
37. Linda —, of "Dallas"
38. Solitary
39. States further
40. Type of muffin
42. Light brown
44. Cow's cry
45. In favor of
48. Apiece: abbr.

6

ACROSS

1. Stitch
4. Concorde: abbr.
7. Recipe direction
11. Bright star
12. Falsehood
13. Sharpen
14. Prayer ender
15. Lodging place
16. Formerly
17. Held in check: hyph. wd.
19. Trying experience
21. Sixth sense: abbr.
22. Fishing pole
23. Wrong act
27. "Don Juan" poet
31. High card
32. — the wrong way, annoy
34. Yoko —
35. Discourage (from)
38. Postponed
41. Pen point
43. Ewe's mate
44. Get away
47. McIntosh and Rome Beauty
51. Sufficient space
52. Obtain
54. Facilitate
55. Medicinal plant
56. Become mature
57. Fragrant flower
58. Exchange for cash
59. Doze off
60. Compass direction: abbr.

DOWN

1. Unspecified amount
2. Smooth; level
3. Desired
4. Indoor footwear item
5. Misdeed
6. Pavarotti, for example
7. Poorly made
8. Distinct sound
9. Ancient Peruvian
10. Scottish dance
11. Brief sleep
18. Employ
20. Steal from
23. Angry
24. Hockey surface
25. Harden; jell
26. Failure
28. Singer Orbison
29. Half a pair
30. Indicate agreement
33. Rebuked severely
36. Glossy paint
37. Tear
39. Race-track circuit
40. Current unit
42. Commenced
44. Time periods
45. One and only
46. — as a cucumber
48. Indochinese country
49. To be: Latin
50. Behold
53. Self

ACROSS

1. Horse's morsel
4. Ear part
8. Leader of Iran, formerly
12. Game cube
13. Filled with wonder
14. Mexican treat
15. Made preliminary sketches
17. Squander
18. Lend a hand
19. Tangy
20. Log house
23. Competition
26. Spoken
27. Yearns (for)
28. Laugh sound
29. NY baseballer
30. Goliath's foe
31. Crate
32. At home
33. Wizardry
34. Bee's home
35. Washington, D.C., for one
37. Book leaves
38. Strong beasts
39. Distant
40. Seizes
42. Evening dresses
46. Completed
47. Barley
48. Pod vegetable
49. "Red" planet
50. Actor Griffith
51. Plaything

DOWN

1. Offbeat
2. Atmosphere
3. British afternoon break
4. Caesar's language
5. Was in debt
6. Resting place
7. TV horse, "Mr. —"
8. Begins
9. Hurry
10. Perform, as in a play
11. Garden tool
16. Be unsuccessful
17. Ebbed
19. Restorative medicine
20. Funny
21. Sports stadium
22. Baseball need
23. Polite
24. Push
25. IRS concern
27. Heathen
30. Goes out with
31. Enormous
33. Kitchen appliances
34. Injure
36. Card game
37. Gala event
39. Crease
40. Male cat
41. Ms. Gardner
42. Cooling device
43. Likely (to)
44. Zodiac lion
45. Speak
47. Pa's mate

BIBLE CROSSWORD   MEDIUM

by Marilyn Wing

Bible references in this puzzle are from the King James Version. You'll find it stimulating to solve, and will discover you know more about the Bible than you think you do.

ACROSS

1. — are ye come? *Judg. 11:7*
4. Not many mighty, not many —, are called. *I Cor. 1:26*
9. He heweth him down cedars . . . he planteth an —. *Isa. 44:14*
12. Be thou like a — or a young hart. *Song 2:17*
13. We remember . . . the leeks, and the —s. *Num. 11:5*
14. Lead me, and —de me. *Ps. 31:3*
15. The Lord hath set — him that is godly for himself. *Ps. 4:3*
17. They shall no more rule over the —. *Ezek. 29:15*
19. They shall —, but thou shalt endure. *Ps. 102:26*
21. He — them with bread. *Gen. 47:17*
22. Thou comest . . . with a sword, and with a —. *I Sam. 17:45*
24. The earth did quake, and the — rent. *Matt. 27:51*
28. Ho, —, come forth. *Zech. 2:6*
30. Carry these ten ch— unto the captain . . . and look how thy brethren fare. *I Sam. 17:18*
32. Precept must be upon precept, . . . line upon —. *Isa. 28:10*
33. All that handle the — . . shall come down from their ships. *Ezek. 27:29*
35. Set me upon a very high mou—. *Ezek. 40:2*
37. Put it upon . . . the great — of their right foot. *Ex. 29:20*
38. I am . . . the bright and morning —. *Rev. 22:16*
40. Ye younger, submit yourselves unto the —. *I Pet. 5:5*
42. Doth the ha— fly? *Job 39:26*
43. The — cometh not, but for to steal. *St. John 10:10*
45. Who hath measured the waters . . . and — out heaven? *Isa. 40:12*
47. Now ye are full, — ye are rich. *I Cor. 4:8*
49. They went up with winding —. *I Ki. 6:8*
52. He struck it into the . . . kettle, or —. *I Sam. 2:14*
56. Give me my wives and my chi—. *Gen. 30:26*
57. The king —se very early in the morning. *Dan. 6:19*
58. This is an heinous —. *Job 31:11*
60. To Seth . . . there was born a son; and he called his name —s. *Gen. 4:26*
61. Cast the — on the right side of the ship. *St. John 21:6*
62. He . . . hath the sharp sword with two —. *Rev. 2:12*
63. A man shall nourish a young —, and two sheep. *Isa. 7:21*

DOWN

1. He can — himself in it. *Isa. 28:20*
2. Now abideth faith, —, charity. *I Cor. 13:13*
3. Ye observe days, and months, . . . and —. *Gal. 4:10*
4. Eye hath —, (2 words) nor ear heard. *I Cor. 2:9*
5. Put — thy shoes. *Ezek. 24:17*
6. —d the sacrifice with cords. *Ps. 118:27*
7. He dealt to every one . . . a — of bread. *I Chr. 16:3*
8. — into his gates with thanksgiving. *Ps. 100:4*
9. Four days — I was fasting. *Acts 10:30*
10. I will cover the — with a cloud. *Ezek. 32:7*
11. My beloved is mine, and I am —. *Song 2:16*

16. Her grapes are fully —. *Rev. 14:18*
18. They . . . offered sacrifice unto the —. *Acts 7:41*
20. Make —, and get thee quickly out. *Acts 22:18*
23. Darius . . . was made king over the —. *Dan. 9:1*
25. Jerusalem shall be called a —y of truth. *Zech. 8:3*
26. I — that my redeemer liveth. *Job 19:25*
27. —, and ye shall find. *Matt. 7:7*
28. It was a great —, like the host of God. *I Chr. 12:22*
29. He would keep the — which he had sworn. *Deut. 7:8*
31. They shall be as thorns in your —. *Judg. 2:3*
34. He shall send thunder and —n. *I Sam. 12:17*
36. Thorns shall come up, . . . — and brambles. *Isa. 34:13*

39. A time to —, and a time to sew. *Eccles. 3:7*
41. He — all the words of the law. *Josh. 8:34*
44. The violent take it by —. *Matt. 11:12*
46. He shall —t thy paths. *Prov. 3:6*
48. They spake the — of God. *Acts 4:31*
50. The same became mighty men, . . . men of —wn. *Gen. 6:4*
51. Wash me, and I shall be whiter than —. *Ps. 51:7*
52. How — we know the way? *St. John 14:5*
53. Ye — the salt of the earth. *Matt. 5:13*
54. Ye shall divide the land by —. *Num. 33:54*
55. Day and —ht shall not cease. *Gen. 8:22*
59. Be merciful unto —. *Ps. 26:11*

ACROSS

1. Compassion
6. Afghanistan's capital
11. Esprit de corps
12. Mythical flier
14. Psyche unit
15. Seder, e.g.
17. Engrossed
18. Certain noble: French
20. Dudgeon
22. Fairway concern
23. Astringent
25. Ball of yarn
27. Continent: abbr.
28. Psalms word
30. Asked
32. Even
34. Bristle
35. Haughty contempt
38. Religious groups
41. Print measure
42. Wedge
44. Actor Calhoun
45. Word from Scrooge
47. Prearrangement
49. Japanese honorific
50. Turkish titles of respect
52. French artist
54. Washington's location: abbr.
55. Modern
57. Czarist decrees
59. Distorts, as data
60. Assembly of churches

DOWN

1. Spacecraft unit
2. Vocalized pause
3. Churchill's "few": abbr.
4. See 25-Across
5. Time periods
6. Feline offspring
7. Electric current: abbr.
8. Soap or chocolate unit
9. Russian river
10. Wolflike
11. Mythical king
13. Substitute's position
16. H.H. Munro
19. Groups of devotees
21. Apiaries
24. Lasses
26. Saltpeter
29. A whole lot
31. Tapachula treats
33. Oversees
35. Exclude
36. Mental pictures
37. 1949 alliance: abbr.
39. Interchanged
40. Becomes meshed, for short
43. Hindu mentors
46. Taxi
48. Slow
51. Bishopric
53. Earth color
56. Compass point
58. Kipling's "Just — Stories"

ACROSS

1. Hemingway's nickname
5. Second Greek letter
9. Easter-Sunday event
11. Uprising
13. Program
14. Mystery
15. Sri Lankan export
16. Took a chair
18. Throw, as a fishing line
19. Take away (from)
22. Rest
25. Stalemate
26. "Yalie"
29. Energy type
31. Bar member
33. Dog's foot
34. Movie studio
36. Military blockade
37. Amid
39. Ticket cost
42. Young child
43. Gawain's title
46. Cook too long
48. Quiche ingredient
51. Judge of Israel
52. Publicize; announce
53. Be excessively fond of (with "on")
54. Designate

DOWN

1. Folio
2. Neighborhood
3. Pastoral god
4. Append
5. Gazzara or Vereen
6. Eject
7. Garment for Caesar
8. Money for the poor
9. Cash of tennis fame
10. Compass heading
11. Wholesale's opposite
12. Make lace
17. Wyeth's field
19. Sight at Aswan
20. Banish
21. Stop
22. Blame: slang
23. Airport listing: abbr.
24. Cow's sound
26. Look over
27. Journey segment
28. Hibernia: abbr.
30. Alabama crop
32. Prevail
35. *Zwei* or *deux*
37. Tam's kin
38. Engrave
39. Driving hazard
40. Eager
41. Change the décor
43. Juncture
44. Man or Wight
45. Stoplight color
47. Female deer
49. Biddy
50. Pitching stat: abbr.

MEDIUM

Puzzles 1 and 2 have been started for you to give you your initial clues. Use both the definitions and the definition numbers as aids in supplying the words and the black squares to go into the diagram. Remember, the pattern of black squares is symmetrical. The example below shows the meaning of symmetry of the black squares in the diagram. When you have discovered the correct placement of a black square, its mate can be inserted in a corresponding position on the opposite side of the diagram. If you are still having difficulty solving Diagramless puzzles, see opposite page for information about a leaflet you can send for. Starting boxes for the other puzzles are listed on THE LAST PAGE.

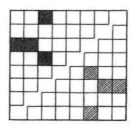

ACROSS

1. Noah's vessel
4. Muffler or babushka
9. Dairy animal
12. Newsman Rather
13. Eiffel —, Paris structure
14. Mimic
15. Out of the ordinary
17. Relieves (a pain)
19. President Carter's middle name
20. Not speaking
21. Loses freshness, as lettuce
23. Zoo compartments
24. Fruit-juice drinks
25. Footways
26. Laugh sound
28. Guided the way
29. Nun's garb
30. Pitcherlike container
31. Scale tone
32. Start
33. Walking stick
34. Alcott's "Little —"
35. Is in need of
36. Shoulder wraps
38. Hide, as one's face
39. Cowboy's rope
40. Satisfied
43. Actor Carney
44. Routine task
46. Paving substance
47. Kickoff gadget
48. Flying toys
49. Secret agent

DOWN

1. TV commercials
2. Knock sharply
3. Bent down
4. Mixes
5. Shipment from West Virginia
6. Hole punch
7. Concerning
8. Cargo
9. Lawsuits
10. Unlock
11. Compass heading
16. Mousers
18. Beerlike beverages
20. Shiny fabric
21. Berlin divider
22. Thought
23. Crude house of logs
25. Book parts
26. Big piece, as of bread
27. Grows older

29. Evergreen tree
30. Blazers, for example
32. Curtsies
33. Play's personnel
34. Haste makes this
35. Divisions of traffic
36. Bed plank
37. Rabbit's kin
38. Greater amount
40. Portable bed
41. Short sleep
42. Make an effort
45. Short greeting

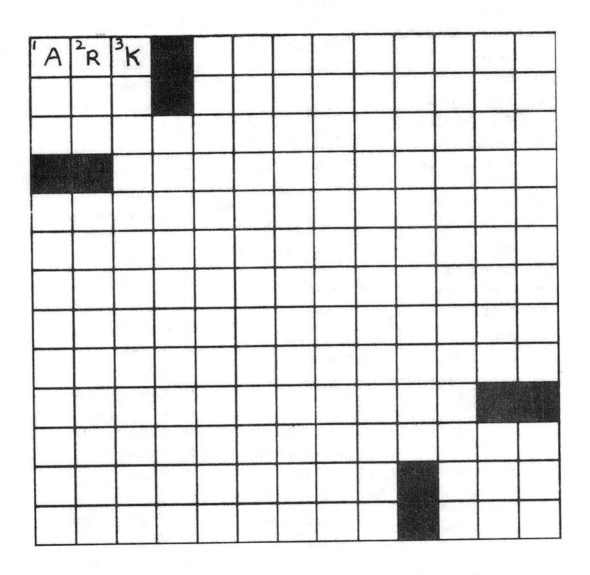

This Diagramless is 17 boxes wide by 17 boxes deep.

ACROSS

1. Cease
5. Pre-nuptial party
7. Encountered
10. Also
11. Ireland : poetic
13. Egyptian river
14. Freshwater fish
15. Grain-storage building
16. Be aware of
17. Shoestring
18. Guided
19. Spruce, e.g.
20. Creative skill
21. Goad
22. Quiet
25. Lawyer's charge
26. Trained observer
28. Embrace
31. Certain
32. Defective
33. Spinning toys
35. Having small depressions
37. Bed boards
39. Cherry seed
40. Percussion instruments
42. Lose one's balance
44. Gross minus expenses
45. Scheme
46. Egyptian cobra
49. Remain
50. Gives for a time
51. Strike, as a fly
53. Row, as of opera seats
54. A Great Lake
55. "Let one's — down," be relaxed
56. State further
57. Number of Commandments
58. King's son
60. Lampblack

DOWN

1. Store
2. In the direction of
3. Is in debt
4. Great danger
5. Painful
6. Stir up
7. Dug for ore
8. Otherwise
9. Golfer's peg
10. Strategies
12. Show agreement
13. Infamous Roman fiddler
14. Small wagons
16. City roads
17. — Vegas, Nevada
21. For each
23. Noisy
24. Entice
25. Fashion craze
27. Bowling game
28. Scoundrel
29. Auctioneer's word
30. Ship mast
32. Wager
34. Dwarfed
36. Gratuity
38. Slander
41. Pigpen
42. Killed
43. Bowling alley
45. Minute skin opening
46. Timber tree
47. Trade
48. Sets of two
49. — with, support
50. Tennis term
52. Group of three
53. Diplomacy
59. Negative reply

1 2 3 4

13

ACROSS

1. Southern State: abbr.
4. Smack
8. "Moby Dick" captain
12. Actor Chaney
13. Molten rock
14. Ran hastily
15. While
16. Small motorized vehicle: hyph. wd.
18. Dog or cat
19. Flag feature
21. Great wonder
23. "— Maria"
24. For goodness —!
26. Mr. Sullivan
28. Detest
30. Mr. Brubeck and others
31. Richmond's State: abbr.
32. Pub brew
33. Country roads
34. Decade number
35. Musical tone
36. Sinks one's teeth into
37. Walking stick
38. Atop
39. Above
40. Pave (a road)
41. Mr. Lincoln, for short
42. Sea robber
45. Heavy weight
47. Retitle
50. Handbill
51. Poker stake
53. Disappeared
54. Mimic
55. Troublesome one
56. Is in debt
57. Males

DOWN

1. Woe is me!
2. Misplaced
3. One
4. Slant
5. Dress trim
6. Ms. Gardner
7. Golf score
8. By
9. Actress Lange
10. Exist
11. Wager
16. Donate
17. Helps oneself to
20. Put in order of preference
22. Basketball great Unseld
24. More rational
25. Thoroughfares: abbr.
26. Level
27. Copenhagen resident
28. Saintly aura
29. Actor Alda
30. Engagement
33. Internal organ
34. Scarlett's home
36. Baseballer Lemon
37. Show concern
40. Multiplied by
41. Picnic pests
42. Window section
43. Record (music)
44. First garden
45. Faucet
46. Single
48. Self
49. Currently
52. Famous film alien: abbr.
54. Before noon: abbr.

ACROSS

1. Unappetizing fare
5. In — of
9. Mountain pass
12. Take off
13. Island off Ireland
14. King, to Pierre
15. Be hawkish: 4 wds.
18. Popular Xmas gift in recent years: abbr.
19. Large duck
20. Jack —, noted lean-eater
23. Reveal
25. *Et* —
26. Tedious
27. In shape
30. Conforms: 3 wds.
33. Observe
34. Currier's partner
35. Formerly
36. Scott, of a renowned Supreme Court case
37. Great quantity
38. Shock
41. Farm sound
42. Misbehaves: 4 wds.
48. — carte: 2 wds.
49. Having a share of: 2 wds.
50. Idyllic spot
51. Legal matter
52. Midday
53. Scatters

DOWN

1. Speedy mode of travel: abbr.
2. Mauna —
3. Hardwood
4. Triumph
5. Actor in "The Wizard of Oz"
6. A Gershwin
7. Pitcher part
8. Experience
9. Battery plate
10. First-rate: 2 wds.
11. Landing place
16. Function
17. Be located
20. Cautious
21. Gambol
22. Stir up
23. Prepared, as fish
24. Social insects
26. Still burning
27. Elegant
28. Indian of Peru
29. "— Wolf," Michael J. Fox film
31. Steakhouse order
32. Settings
36. German article
37. Clumsy sort
38. Seaweed
39. Soccer great
40. School groups: abbr.
41. W. Germany's capital
43. Half a pair, to Juan
44. Very
45. Reply from the bride or groom: 2 wds.
46. Fresh
47. Print measures

DIAGONAL CROSSWORD   HARD

by John Greenman

Solve this special crossword just as you would a regular crossword, except that the words are written into the diagram DIAGONALLY, either downward or upward, but always from left to right. The answers to the definitions for 1-Upward and 3-Downward have been entered to start you off. Half the boxes have been shaded to help you follow the paths of the diagonals.

UPWARD

1. Possessed
4. Infuriation
8. United
10. Sections of wall covering
12. Amphitheater
13. Ms. Gless of TV
14. Strives hard
16. Onassis, for short
18. Indicates approval
21. Section of a textbook: 2 wds.
23. Play section
26. Takes by force
29. Actress Verdon and others
31. Calmed
33. Waist-length jackets
35. High-protein food
36. Subtle emanation
38. Buddy
39. Perched
40. Understand
42. Caesar's 7
43. Borzoi or corgi
44. Fastidious
45. — out, supplement
46. Pittsburgh product
49. Goes beyond
52. Newman-Redford film (with "The")
55. Authored
57. Miscalculation
59. Becomes wearisome
60. Tight closure
61. McMahon and Begley
62. Elicitors
65. Designed for sight
69. — which way, in complete disorder
70. Involve
71. Impressions
72. Microscopic organism
73. Roads: abbr.

DOWNWARD

1. Urges on
2. On a cruise
3. Modern dance great, Ruth St. —
4. Stadium cheer
5. Literary collection
6. Berliner: abbr.
7. Stretch
8. Full of grease
9. Schottische, for one
10. Greek letters
11. TV reception problem
14. Mrs., in Madrid: abbr.
15. Matched group
16. Jargons
17. — Jackson, "Mr. October"
19. Rely (on)
20. Moves sinuously
21. Book illustration
22. Modify
24. Prose work
25. Wife of Geraint and her namesakes
26. "Ties the knot"
27. Fighting (with)
28. Take to court
30. Toboggan
31. Donkey
32. Billy — Williams
34. Family member, for short
37. Knock
41. Knowledgeable ones
47. Before, poetically
48. Cared for
50. Actor Grant and golfer Middlecoff
51. Raised railways
53. Church area
56. Nickname for Helen
58. Goes on a ramble
64. Artist, Rockwell —
66. French holy woman: abbr.
67. Former union of Egypt and Syria: abbr.
68. Objective

16

MEDIUM

ACROSS

1. Window support
6. Locations
11. Posted
12. Handsome youth
14. Highest point
15. Dialect
17. Recording: abbr.
18. Dessert order
19. Motionless
20. Caspian, e.g.
21. Musical tone
22. Ecstasy
23. Habit
24. Annex
25. Chess piece
26. Highway
27. Omen
28. Freshwater fish
29. A dozen dozen
31. Stir up
32. Be quiet!
34. Long and slender
35. Discovered
36. Westward —!
37. Breakfast selection
38. Chili need
39. Gymnast's item
40. Near
41. Dens
42. Dwell
43. Up-to-date
45. Glossy paint
47. Tip
48. Put down

DOWN

1. Skin treatment
2. Hoarfrost
3. Pub order
4. Part of us
5. Publisher's word
6. Takes a cruise
7. Adored one
8. Male cat
9. Print measure
10. Mum
11. Light-colored wood
13. Overabundance
16. Thin, round object
19. Toils
20. Dinner course
22. Energetic
23. Universe
26. Drizzles
27. Ballad
28. Advise
29. Glint
30. Convertible car: slang
31. Bellow
32. Barber, at times
33. Stopover
35. Boxing ploy
38. Farm sight
39. Mimic
41. Hawaiian garland
42. Statute
44. Perform
46. Never!

ACROSS

1. Cut off (branches)
4. Smack
8. Location
12. Rowing blade
13. Ocean motion
14. Say grace
15. Avoid walking on: 2 wds.
17. "The Eternal City"
18. Surface (a road)
19. Coal sources
20. Trite
22. Reach across
24. Charter
25. Alarms suddenly
29. Poe's "before"
30. Brag
31. Keatslike poem
32. Ruins
34. Once more
35. Pied Piper followers
36. Zodiac units
37. Show off, in a way
40. Shade trees
41. Bauxite, etc.
42. Carnival attraction
46. Roster
47. Impulse
48. Word on a bill
49. Specks
50. Horn sound
51. Powerful explosive: abbr.

DOWN

1. — Angeles
2. Grain morsel
3. Makes ready
4. Kitchen fixture
5. Dwell (at)
6. Lemony drink
7. For each
8. Short, fast run
9. Golf club
10. No longer wild
11. Spud buds
16. Lacking color
19. Trade center
20. Cast off, as leaves
21. Become exhausted
22. Remains behind
23. Free ticket
25. Chimney grime
26. Unlikely derby winner: 2 wds.
27. Biblical garden
28. Does crewelwork
30. Unruly child
33. Has faith in
34. Intentions
36. Emulate Rip Van Winkle
37. Auctioneer's cry
38. Threesome
39. "Take five"
40. Maugham classic, "The Razor's —"
42. U-boat, for short
43. Make angry
44. Possess
45. Sopping

18

MEDIUM

ACROSS

1. Reverence
4. Scorch
8. Festive occasion
12. "Sly" creature
13. Stockings
14. Kiln
15. Spinning toy
16. Utensil
18. — Stanley Gardner
20. Warns
21. Cubed
23. Begin
24. Fixed way of doing something
25. Leave out
26. Gloomy
29. Near
30. Originates (from)
33. Behold!
34. Car fuel
36. Flooring material
37. Relieve
39. Giggle sound
41. Shaving need
42. Sailors
44. Greek cheese
45. Receivers of foreign goods
47. Allow
50. Graceful rhythm
51. Lily's kin
52. Make a mistake
53. Elm or oak
54. Citrus fruit
55. Some

DOWN

1. Astern
2. Pay court to
3. Anticipate
4. Offspring
5. Residence
6. Viper
7. Kin
8. TV oldie "— Pyle, USMC"
9. Prevents
10. Loaned
11. Picnic pests
17. Gladden
19. Marsh grass
21. Haul
22. Jot
23. Grin
25. Of the East
27. And
28. Performer
31. Upper atmosphere
32. Chair
35. Kind of metal fastener
38. Flowering shrub
40. Act theatrically
41. View again
42. River sand
43. Arabian prince
44. Out of
46. Actor Wallach
48. Sea eagle
49. Attempt

ACROSS

1. Social climber, for one
5. Scaloppine meat
9. More: Spanish
12. Ear lobes
13. Distinct: comb. form
14. Island: French
15. Those who noodge
17. Charlemagne, to Pepin
18. Stating
19. Felt
21. Mrs. Ernie Kovacs
23. TV's Detective Yemana
24. Skirt edge
27. Son of Judah
29. Sandwich filler
32. Title of respect in Istanbul
33. Telegraphed
35. First baseman Carew
36. Ripped
38. Priest's robe: var. sp.
39. — Jima
40. Okay!
42. Ladies of La Mancha: Spanish (abbr.)
44. Rural *pied-à-terre*
47. Contend
51. Author Levin
52. Bubbled, as a painted area
54. Saint: Spanish
55. Chain element
56. Calamitous
57. Finis
58. "Giant" author Ferber
59. Spotted

DOWN

1. Lacunas
2. Olive genus
3. Uncomplicated
4. Knot anew
5. Old Dominion
6. Netherlands city
7. Ditties
8. Misplaces
9. Show Me State
10. Sunburn remedy
11. Dispatch
16. Bestow upon
20. In no manner
22. Monroe and Hines
24. Kepi or taj
25. One's self
26. Old Line State
28. Cornhusker State
30. Presently
31. Ruckus
34. Administered
37. Conger
41. Marten
43. Toboggans
44. Woodworker's aid
45. Where Tabriz is
46. Skidded
48. Lake near Buffalo
49. "The Cotton Club" star
50. Idyllic spot
53. Motel of yore

20

ACROSS

1. Winter vehicle
5. Froth
9. Foot digit
12. Peel
13. Prefix meaning "against"
14. Pie — mode: 2 wds.
15. In the present condition: 2 wds.
16. Adolescent: hyph. wd.
18. Bed linen
20. Plant starter
21. Football-game cheer
23. Fast
27. Striking difference
32. Change addresses
33. Street: abbr.
34. Assumed name
36. Cookware item
37. Fourth planet
39. Adversary, as in sport
41. Story lines
43. Before: poetic
44. Upon
47. Happening
51. Dreadful
55. Region
56. Raw mineral
57. Noisy
58. Clock face
59. Angry
60. Lower limbs
61. Land measure

DOWN

1. Health resorts
2. Eyelid hair
3. A Great Lake
4. Gobi or Sahara
5. Overweight
6. Small bills
7. Suit to —: 2 wds.
8. One who digs coal
9. Price label
10. Bullfight
11. Hearing organ
17. Eden dweller
19. Scarlett's home
22. Ring of light
24. Vatican resident
25. — the Terrible
26. Fender mishap
27. Collection of tents
28. Egg-shaped
29. Fiddle-playing Roman emperor
30. Drink slowly
31. Sticky strip, for short
35. Painful
38. Leading actor
40. Reno's state
42. Motionless
45. Woodwind instrument
46. Stopper
48. TV's Sevareid
49. Close (at hand)
50. Story
51. Male cat
52. Time period
53. Crimson
54. Sullivan and Asner

ACROSS

1. Soap unit
4. Letter necessity
9. Dove's call
12. — carte: 2 wds.
13. Traveller's stop
14. Uncooked
15. Ms. MacGraw
16. Exist
17. Worship
19. Identical
21. Winter precipitation
22. Nutmeg or thyme
24. Slim
27. Gasp for air
28. Malice
29. Behold!
30. Donkey
31. Breeding horses
32. 1/60 minute: abbr.
33. Take — easy, relax
34. Household task
35. Punch: slang
36. Sisters' sons
38. Young horses
39. Lubricates
40. "On Golden —" 1981 film
41. Put brush to canvas
43. That man
44. Under the weather
47. Possess
48. Run away to wed
50. Needle's threading-hole
51. Moist; damp
52. Classifies; ranks
53. Crimson or scarlet

DOWN

1. Sheep's cry
2. Everyone
3. Dried grapes
4. Disgrace
5. Ripped
6. Enjoyed dinner
7. Augusta's State: abbr.
8. Earth and Mars
9. Group; clique
10. Rower's need
11. Be in debt
18. Fully cooked
20. Play a role
21. Playground attraction
22. Madrid's country
23. Wallpaper stickum
24. Boot-heel devices
25. Vote in
26. Stones
28. Stores (away)
31. Refuge
32. Member of an army
34. Face feature
35. Family member
37. Pencil tip
38. Arrives
40. Smoker's implement
41. Comic-book "noise"
42. Wonder
43. Very warm
45. Soap ingredient
46. Guided
49. Scale note

25

22

ACROSS

1. Largest continent
5. Venetian blind segment
9. Chum
12. Hankering
13. Pause
15. Time spans
16. Writing fluid
17. Tumult
18. Printer's measure
19. Mr. Carney
20. Heats
21. Factory facility
24. Gratuity
25. Large animal
26. Word with "dial" and "deck"
27. Crow's cry
30. Calculates a total
31. Chatter
32. Sit for the camera
33. Affirmative
34. Leap on one foot
35. Got up
36. Halloween word
37. Roused from sleep
38. Narrow boat
41. Mr. Vigoda
42. As stated
44. Kiln
45. — Baba
46. Passport endorsement
48. Set aside
50. Always
51. Founded: abbr.
52. Speed contest
53. Turner and Kennedy

DOWN

1. Assistant
2. Herd's rush
3. Slippery
4. Exclamations
5. Word with "tail" and "sleeve"
6. Pre-Easter period
7. Inquire
8. Scale tone
9. Match
10. Tiny particle
11. Allows
14. Snare
19. Picnic pest
20. Be victorious
22. Boys
23. Donkey
24. Vat
25. Inlet
26. Tree fluid
27. Chef
28. Evaluated
29. Tiny
31. Sticky stuff
32. Expert, for short
34. Garden tool
35. Reverence
36. Fido's treat
37. Put up with
38. Apple center
39. Streets: abbr.
40. Baby bird's home
41. Actor Guinness
43. Paddles
45. Ms. Gardner
46. Animal doc, for short
47. "— Got a Secret"
49. Train system: abbr.

ACROSS

1. Microbe
5. Woodchuck, for one
11. Locality, in law
12. Royal grandeur
13. Small map within a larger one
14. Bedouin, for one
15. 60 minutes: abbr.
16. Form of poker
17. Whisk
18. Word with "horse" or "breeze"
19. Bullring cry
20. Dull pain
21. Banal humor: slang
22. Remainder
24. Force out of bed
25. Breakfast item
27. Pluck (a banjo)
30. Airman
34. Geological periods
35. British gun
36. Scoring tennis-serve
37. Oil-drilling equipment
38. Two of a kind
39. Ms. Moreno
40. College degree: abbr.
41. Skater Heiden
42. Entree accompaniment
43. Benefactors
45. Fresh, pure air: slang
46. First-born
47. "The Way We —," song

DOWN

1. Kindly
2. Happens as a consequence of
3. Regretted
4. New York museum, for short
5. An Osmond
6. Slightly open
7. Confederate soldier, for short
8. Author's submission: abbr.
9. Additional ones
10. Despot
11. Cap brim
12. School subject
17. Hare's tail
18. French coin
20. Oldest son on TV's "Bonanza"
21. Soft-drink flavor
23. Papers signed by a debtor: abbr.
24. Precipitation
26. Always
27. Mexican poncho
28. Pertaining to a clan
29. Taunt: slang
31. Fashion to fit
32. Word in a gasoline ad
33. Charles —, English author
35. Canonized one
38. Affirmative arguments
39. Demolish
41. Before, poetically
42. Female bear
44. Gridiron score: abbr.

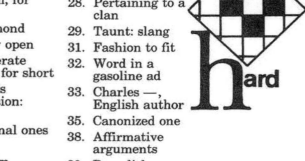

hard

24

ACROSS

1. Baby powder ingredient
5. Unruly child
9. Father
12. Bread spread, for short
13. Painful cry
14. — de Janeiro
15. Unwrap
16. Height, as of a plane in flight
18. Apple center
20. Titles
21. Capital of Greece
24. Omelet-maker's need
25. Task
26. Certain scale notes
27. Faucet
30. Stop!
31. Boat paddle
32. Ceremony
33. Ram's mate
34. Combine; blend
35. Shoestrings
36. False god
38. Admission token
39. Hermit
41. Timid
42. Guacamole fruits
44. Sunrise direction
48. Males
49. Roster
50. Oak or elm
51. Prefix meaning "before"
52. Gels
53. Mr. Musial

DOWN

1. Also
2. High mountain
3. Actor Majors
4. Musical performance
5. Wild hogs
6. Regulation
7. Play segment
8. Items
9. Turkey eater's request
10. Assistant
11. Accomplishes
17. Chasing game
19. Single bill
21. Dull pain
22. Melt
23. Golf feat: 3 wds.
24. Hearing organ
26. Loose; slack
28. To —, exactly: 2 wds.
29. Nuisance
31. Lubricate
32. Tennis "paddles"
34. Fable endings
35. Fib
37. 12th month: abbr.
38. Exams
39. Light fixture
40. Above
41. Greatest amount
43. Gaming cube
45. Mr. Carney
46. Ocean
47. Decade number

ACROSS

1. Intention
4. Otherwise
8. Put down (carpeting)
11. Decorative edging
13. Legal claim
14. Memorable period
15. Hawaiian windstorm
16. Sound-engineer's bane
18. Invalidate
20. For each
21. Choose
24. Duplicate
28. That man's
30. Dressed pelts
32. "— Indigo"
33. Fuss; excitement
34. Makes a stab at
36. Guided
37. Many
39. Ancient Roman garb
40. Alphabet letter
41. Knack
43. Sub detector
45. Pilot's record
47. Window pane
50. Health-club offering
55. Against
56. Very small
57. Hautboy
58. Shoo!
59. Shade tree
60. Canvas shelter
61. Stare at

DOWN

1. Aleutian island
2. Wood's companion, in golf
3. Gopher State
4. Yuletide helper
5. Fib
6. Ooze (out)
7. Terminated
8. Grassland: poetic
9. Bowlike line
10. Tibetan ox
12. Handle roughly
17. Derby rim
19. Departed
22. Brusque
23. The wise men and the blind mice
25. Endurance
26. Shoe tips
27. At —, quarreling
28. Word with "back" or "baked"
29. Object of worship
31. Trumpet-shaped lily
35. Crooned
38. Rural sight
42. R2D2, for one
44. Woeful cry
46. Scoff (at)
48. Remain
49. Location
50. Fill with wonder
51. Snaky fish
52. Sleep phenomenon: abbr.
53. Swindle: slang
54. Fix (a price)

ACROSS

1. Fitzgerald, of song
5. Large amount
9. Nourished
12. — out, exhaust
13. Lazy
14. Charlotte —, of TV's "Facts of Life"
15. Film director, Blake —
17. Racket
19. Social insect
20. Was in harmony
21. Weave, as a rug
24. Hints
25. Coolidge, of song
26. Mr. Presley
27. Audiophile's buy: abbr.
29. Frost
30. Ordinary
31. Mr. Costello
32. Part of us
33. Mature
34. Musical quality
35. Journeys
36. Gem
37. Saint's tomb
39. Fish's appendage
40. Emulate Monet
41. Reference book
45. Malt brew
46. Perry Mason's creator Gardner
48. Woman's name
49. Pole; dowel
50. Enjoy a novel
51. Double

DOWN

1. Female sheep
2. Conducted
3. Statute
4. "Lawrence of —,"film classic
5. Conceal
6. McMahon and others
7. Mr. Pacino
8. Flightless bird
9. Fast-food order
10. Facilitate
11. Heroic feat
16. Blushing
18. Raw metals
20. Cartoon chipmunk
21. Bowler feature
22. Oriental-food staple
23. Dined
24. Talons
26. Run away to wed
27. Volcanic peak
28. Contest
30. Office machine
31. Close to the ground
33. Smile
34. Lessee
35. Took a stab at
36. Mr. Nabors
37. Shadow box
38. Nimbus
39. Escaped
41. Southern State: abbr.
42. At once
43. Boxing great
44. Dismiss: slang
47. Concerning

ACROSS

1. Sheep's sound
4. Acknowledge
9. Ocean
12. Lubricate
13. Renter's document
14. Shake (a tail)
15. Most courageous
17. Rub out
19. Annoy
20. Feats; tricks
21. Gift of money, as for research
24. Borsht ingredients
25. Misplace
26. Listens to
27. Pa's mate
29. Big deer
30. Elvis hit, "— Shook Up"
31. Leap
32. Overhead train
33. Closes
35. Peel
36. Wading places
37. Curved roofs
38. Begins
40. Fib
41. Squander
42. Helena's State
46. Likely (to)
47. Depart
49. Mongrel
50. "Busy" insect
51. Tear into strips
52. Explosive: abbr.

DOWN

1. Mr. Dylan
2. Word with "line" or "mail"
3. Chicken — king: 2 wds.
4. Watchful
5. Writing table
6. Exercise pad
7. "Eight — Enough"
8. Wobble
9. Graceful water birds
10. Sunrise direction
11. Matures
16. Climbing plant
18. Wheel furrows
20. Marine mammals
21. Joy
22. Bun
23. Inquire
24. Alternatives to suspenders
26. Transports (a load), as by truck
27. To a greater degree
28. Orangutans
31. Lunch meat
33. Kind; type
34. Lodging places
35. Keats, for one
36. Sticky stuff
37. Had a meal
38. Sailor: slang
39. Adhesive strip
40. Deep affection
42. Deface
43. Play a role
44. Convent occupant
45. Museum sight
48. "What did you say?"

BIBLE CROSSWORD

by MARILYN WING

Bible references in this puzzle are from the King James Version. You'll find it stimulating to solve, and may discover you know more Bible than you think you do.

ACROSS

1. I will — them with a fan. *Jer. 15:7*

4. Walk in the light of your fire, and in the —s that ye have kindled. *Isa. 50:11*

9. Make ready wherewith I may —, ... and serve me, till I have eaten. *Luke 17:8*

12. How long will it be — they believe me? *Num. 14:11*

13. I have decked my bed ... with fine —. *Prov. 7:16*

14. His name shall be called ... The —nce of Peace. *Isa. 9:6*

15. The Lord himself shall — from heaven. *I Thess. 4:16*

17. Pay me that thou —. *Matt. 18:28*

19. —n thy mouth wide. *Ps. 81:10*

20. Ye shall not eat ... neither ten days, nor — days. *Num. 11:19*

21. The river of Kishon — them away. *Judg. 5:21*

24. In —s of rich apparel ... made of cedar. *Ezek. 27:24*

25. The king had at sea a — ... with the navy of Hiram. *I Kin. 10:22*

26. He scattereth the hoar —. *Ps. 147:16*

27. —, I am with you. *Matt. 28:20*

29. They shall be ... as the sm— out of the chimney. *Hos. 13:3*

30. They ... — themselves in the multitude of their riches. *Ps. 49:6*

31. Christ died — us. *Rom. 5:8*

32. — are his people. *Ps. 100:3*

33. I was left —, and saw this great vision. *Dan. 10:8*

34. The harvest is —, the summer is ended. *Jer. 8:20*

35. Whosoever shall compel thee to go —, (2 words) go with him twain. *Matt. 5:41*

36. Thy — and thy nativity is of the land of Canaan. *Ezek. 16:3*

37. The — ... shall pick it out and the young eagles shall eat it. *Prov. 30:17*

39. Thou anointest my head with —. *Ps. 23:5*

40. He shall make —s for the harm that he hath done. *Lev. 5:16*

41. The God of —, of Isaac, and of Jacob, appeared. *Ex. 3:16*

45. How — we know the way? *St. John 14:5*

46. The word of God is ... sharper than any two-— sword. *Heb. 4:12*

48. He casteth forth his — ...: who can stand before his cold? *Ps. 147:17*

49. —rave the two stones with the names. *Ex. 28:11*

50. Let them shut the —, and bar them. *Neh. 7:3*

51. He ... — my feet upon a rock. *Ps. 40:2*

DOWN

1. He — them with bread. *Gen. 47:17*

2. I am not as other men —. *Luke 18:11*

3. There shall the great owl make her —t. *Isa. 34:15*

4. They all slumbered and —. *Matt. 25:5*

5. Fetch olive branches, and — branches. *Neh. 8:15*

6. Sodom — Gomorrah

7. The —d sea

8. Thou ... — what thou oughtest to do. *I Ki. 2:9*

9. We will not hide it . . . how that our money is —. *Gen. 47:18*
10. New wine will b— the bottles, and be spilled. *Luke 5:37*
11. He shall not . . . have —, nor have mercy. *Jer. 21:7*
16. This is the — of the letter that they sent. *Ezra. 4:11*
18. Many shall come from the east and —. *Matt. 8:11*
20. Gallio cared for none of — things. *Acts 18:17*
21. It was white as —. *Ps. 68:14*
22. We — or sleep. *I Thess. 5:10*
23. Adam called his wife's name —. *Gen. 3:20*
24. Like a — or a swallow, so did I chatter. *Isa. 38:14*
26. The foolishness of the — is folly. *Prov. 14:24*
27. I have found my sheep which was —. *Luke 15:6*
28. From that time f— came they no more. *Neh. 13:21*

30. He hath — their eyes . . . that they should not see. *St. John 12:40*
31. Be not — from me. *Ps. 22:11*
33. Prayer ending
34. They . . . delivered him to Pontius —te. *Matt. 27:2*
35. Thou mightest still the enemy and the —er. *Ps. 8:2*
36. — make their nests. *Ps. 104:17*
37. The — is not to the swift. *Eccles. 9:11*
38. Thou art —, (2 words) and not God. *Ezek. 28:2*
39. The aged men be s—, grave. *Titus 2:2*
41. Four days — I was fasting. *Acts 10:30*
42. My beloved is mine, and I am —. *Song 2:16*
43. I have seen God f— to face. *Gen. 32:30*
44. They — Moses and Aaron, who stood in the way. *Ex. 5:20*
47. — as he hath said. *I Ki. 2:31*

29

hard

ACROSS

1. Assert without proof
7. Taints
13. Crown
14. Graduation adornment
15. Approve
16. Day of rest
18. Japanese board game
19. Word with "York" and "Delhi"
21. Cheek color
22. Looked at
23. Isles: French
25. Compass point
26. Silent
27. Slender, graceful women
29. Judged
31. Billiards rod
32. Actress, Rita —
33. Chews hard
36. Musical composition
39. Harness piece
40. Aardvark's tidbit
42. Very: French
43. Hail!
44. Jeer
46. *Oui* or *si*
47. Mi follower
48. Proper use of words
50. Common pronoun
51. Coveted
53. Explores, in a way
55. Canonized ones
56. Hastens

DOWN

1. Handsome fellow
2. Apt (to)
3. "— Boheme"
4. Asner and Wynn
5. Equipment
6. Raise in relief
7. Presented, as a play
8. London gallery
9. Cigar residue
10. Exists
11. Deny
12. Decelerated
17. Motor coach
20. Greet with pleasure
22. Abridgment
24. Froth
26. Intended
28. "In the know": slang
30. Conceit
33. Irritates
34. Cuban capital
35. Dinner offerings
36. Perplexes
37. Poured
38. Evaluate
41. Moniker: French
44. Worry
45. Waterproof canvas
48. Card game
49. Fish eggs
52. Six, in old Rome
54. "Let It —"

ACROSS

1. Certain plane
4. Dinners
9. Recede
12. Past
13. Consumed
14. Female deer
15. Lifts
17. Covet
19. House pets
21. Change
22. Be the same as
25. Dessert choice
27. Litters' smallest members
28. Replies
32. Help
33. Go by air
34. Atlas item
35. Piebald
38. Award
40. Went by bus
41. Appraised
42. T-bone
45. College official
47. Weighed heavily (on)
49. Be present at
53. Atmosphere
54. Daring; courage
56. Lock opener
57. Plaything
58. Fathered
59. Female sheep

DOWN

1. Poke
2. Self
3. Also
4. Alloys, e.g.
5. Sunrise direction
6. Near; by
7. Guided
8. Goes furtively
9. Work on manuscripts
10. Tiresome person
11. Pub offering
16. Shoo!
18. Killed
20. Burned by water
22. Historic periods
23. Clever remark
24. Annul
26. Some
29. Give off
30. Demolish
31. Raced
33. Nourished
36. Serving piece
37. Bus coins
38. Talked nonstop
39. Rave
42. Petty quarrel
43. Threesome
44. Weird
46. Roof edge
48. Agnus —
50. — out, supplement
51. Not old
52. Tint
55. Train system: abbr.

Puzzles 31 and 32 have been started for you to give you your initial clues. Use both the definitions and the definition numbers as aids in supplying the words and the black squares to go into the diagram. Remember, the pattern of black squares is symmetrical. The example below shows the meaning of symmetry of the black squares in the diagram. When you have discovered the correct placement of a black square, its mate can be inserted in a corresponding position on the opposite side of the diagram. If you are still having difficulty solving Diagramless puzzles, see opposite page for information about a leaflet you can send for. Starting boxes for the other puzzles are listed on the last page.

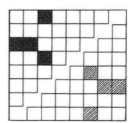

ACROSS

1. Play a role
4. Auction
8. Shoo!
12. Cheerleader's cry
13. Among
14. Story
15. Interlaced
17. Valuable fur
18. Facial feature
19. Sandwich bun
20. Seized
22. Billfolds
25. Grew older
26. Two-wheelers
27. Hello!
28. Footed vase
29. Walks in water
30. Friend; buddy
31. Compass point
32. Tall —, outlandish stories
33. Weep loudly
34. Small hunting dog
36. Plant with velvety petals
37. Feed-bag morsels
38. Saucy; impudent
39. Potatoes
41. Had a collision
44. Relieve
45. Fish-catching device
46. A Gabor
47. Fruit drinks
48. — and ends, remnants
49. Bright color

DOWN

1. Mr. Carney
2. Crow's call
3. Make more dense
4. Shiny fabric
5. So be it!
6. Pot cover
7. Mr. Asner
8. Stable compartments
9. Anchor chain
10. Every one
11. Golf gadget
16. Lean-to
17. Shoe bottoms
19. Leaf-gathering tools
20. Jeer at
21. Concur

22. Broader
23. Melts
24. Foolish
26. Hay bundles
29. Lingers; stays
30. Type of leopard
32. Exchanges
33. Excludes
35. Wake
36. Mountaintops
38. Jab; poke
39. Baltic or Red
40. Cushion
41. Cape —,
    Massachusetts
    vacation-spot
42. First woman
43. Father
45. Santa's sound

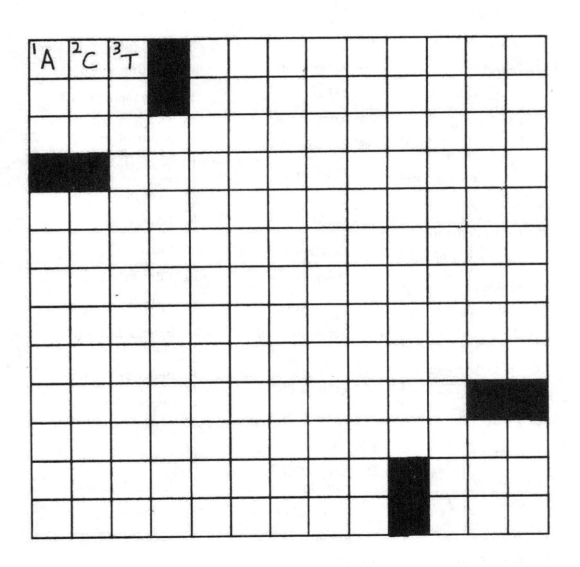

This Diagramless is 17 boxes wide by 17 boxes deep.

ACROSS

1. Feline
4. Summer drinks
6. Trousers
8. Male
11. Satellites
13. Walking sticks
15. Cheers (for)
17. Summery shoes
19. Tiny skin opening
20. Attempt
21. Knocks sharply
23. They have 88 keys
25. Midday
27. Furrower
28. Clock the speed of
29. Spider's creation
32. Rodent
34. Allow
35. Aroma
37. Have on
40. Three trios
41. "Hoofer"
43. Food fish
45. Lad
46. Afternoon socials
48. City roads
50. Slides
52. Rescues
53. Frozen rain
55. Wager
56. Taste with relish
58. Nevada city
59. Unused

DOWN

1. Bottle top
2. Eve's hubby
3. Choir voice
5. Bend forward
7. Nosy one
8. Quite a few
9. Plus
10. Close by
12. Takeoff or landing runway
13. Automobiles
14. Slope
16. Close tightly
17. Ticketless, concealed passengers
18. Ruin
22. A few
24. And not
26. Fishing mesh
29. Was victorious
30. Prepare for publication
31. Incentive pay
33. Five pairs
36. Leases
38. Performs
39. Film spools
41. Spots
42. Speaks bitterly (against)
44. Bedouin, for one
45. Shade of red
47. Lance
49. Actress Arden
51. "Lucky" number
54. Sound quality
57. Propel with oars

PUNANAGRAMS

by Mel Taub

Punanagrams are tricky but fun to solve. Definitions may be jokes or puns on the word wanted, or an anagram of the word itself. Generally there's a straight definition as a clue too. For example, the answer to 8-Down is HOTEL. *The ol'* is the anagram, with "Waldorf" as an additional clue. Roman numerals may be used; the words YOU, ARE, EYE, SEE, etc., might stand for U, R, I and C, respectively; "energy" could stand for the letters N, R, G, or "any" for N E. Consider the definitions from all angles and you will find they do make definite sense. And, have fun!

ACROSS

1. Who did peer ask to say a few words?
8. Double — (gossip-columnist's look-alike)
13. Highly emotional person at barbecue site?
14. Windows on oilers
16. On Oct. 5 a Red behaved extravagantly
17. Mournful sitter: French
18. Maine town runs rings around Reagan
19. Wonders about such as we
21. Try him for verse
22. Drinks for toddlers
23. As outspoken Latin, I avoid vacillation
25. Sounded like Bossy had temper
26. Tea, that is, even
27. Not the clergy of Italy
28. Alien crooner Frankie
29. Eccentric fellow carrying 500 lb. load
31. Chief rates 50-50
33. What do 'e do when 'e want to leave?
34. Make 'otter
35. Associate held up to scorn
39. Damages caused by songs of mischievous fellow

43. Lose a bit of medicine
44. Commercial liable to accommodate
46. She joins Leo in Toledo
47. Sttone of sortt
48. Instrument found in a P.O.
49. He's some guy!
50. She stopped off in Nevada and left
51. Free — (gratuitous lawyer's service)
52. He took Lehar to court
53. Prize for iron BB
55. African who might rib alien
58. Had Ellie seen the goddess?
59. Siam isn't the place for men of spirit
60. What stern landlords insist on
61. Provide too much to eat, as it were

DOWN

1. In Pisa, rod is used to catch fish
2. Turned, in a way, to top dive
3. Jackets used on set
4. Job for a barber
5. Carson is taking nag out
6. Hin this place
7. Frame a Bolshevik deed
8. The ol' Waldorf
9. Mistakes lead to arrest at departure

10. Is idiot to leave number?
11. Rob old pies
12. Home of Lana, too
13. What is the cost to soprano Renata?
15. He plants tree by the sound of it
20. 3,241 of Sawyer's methods
23. Courage? See it emanate from Victrola
24. Broiled in the center
25. Where Mathilda hid out
27. Where to find Nigerian gaols
28. Jumped from the plate
30. What to do if you can't be ready?
32. Pace needed to top me
35. Pranks leading to scrape

36. 7-role actor
37. Incapable of being outstanding
38. T' be under the weather
39. Giant's middle name
40. It is old word for Baal worshiper
41. Viewed favorably, as a stereo
42. Parts of ships where nests are found
45. Where all sad Texans hail from
48. Trees in which snipe nests
49. Is she from Romania? No, no!
51. Town habit
52. Half the border, I gather
54. Gal's predecessor
56. Carol's companion
57. How to make limp blimp

34

ACROSS

1. Cushion
4. Shoe bottoms
9. Recent
12. Epoch
13. Wear away
14. Thoroughfare: abbr.
15. Diminishes
17. Did secretarial work
19. City roads: abbr.
20. Guides
21. Men
24. Red as a —
25. High cards
26. Gentle animal
27. Health resort
30. Actress Farrow
31. Orchard fruits
32. Bunny jump
33. Find the sum of
34. Girl
35. Roused
36. Desire
37. Force
38. Indelible spots
41. To and —
42. Seacoast State
43. Gift
47. Ancient
48. Attempts
50. Caviar
51. Golly!: slang
52. Transmits
53. Ram's mate

DOWN

1. For each
2. Exist
3. Family member
4. Religious subgroups
5. Lode finds
6. — Angeles
7. Singer Ames
8. Hunting dogs
9. Neck back
10. Always
11. Marries
16. Employs
18. Still
20. Fortunetellers
21. Baby's name for mother
22. Tart
23. Heavy metal
24. Creature
26. College officials
27. Display
28. Prod
29. Copycat
31. Mars and Venus
35. Courts
36. Come in first
37. Printing machine
38. Fog and smoke
39. Yarn
40. Assistant
41. Dancer Astaire
43. Brooch
44. Poet's "before"
45. At present
46. Golf peg
49. Scale note

ACROSS

1. Postpone
6. Gounod opera
11. North American nation
12. Underwrite
14. Tolerated
15. Folklore creatures
16. Grooves
17. She loved Narcissus
19. Gym pad
20. Avenues: abbr.
21. Road mishap
22. Athletic contest
23. Retain
24. Throws
25. Lance
27. Color anew
28. Scorched
29. Knight's wife
30. Pub orders
31. Contradict
32. Pull-top
35. Possessive pronoun
36. Spring flower
37. Actress Negri
38. Tell tales
40. Street sign: 2 wds.
42. "Baby —" Fanny Brice character
43. Scrooge et al.
44. Former coins of India
45. Gale

DOWN

1. First appearance
2. Theater signs
3. Covers
4. Expert
5. Swiss singer
6. Struggle
7. — Domini
8. Military entertainment group: abbr.
9. Recap
10. Old poison remedy
11. Red planet
13. Mr. Kefauver
18. Tarboosh, for one
21. Act of daring
22. Mr. Vallee
23. Understands, in Scotland
24. Ms. Lamarr
25. Certain grape
26. "The Music Man" star
27. Kidnappers' demands
28. Tempts; entices
29. Hawaiian garland
31. Gown
32. Pisa attraction
33. Frighten
34. Inlets
36. Actress Chase
37. Coin of 11-Across
39. Heavy weight
41. Young insect

hard

ACROSS

1. Meander
5. Rule-enforcer, for short
8. In the thick of
12. Weaponry: slang
13. Highest note
14. Thespian Thompson
15. Requisite
16. Circus offering
18. Affront
20. Purloins
21. Pinocchio, at times
23. "To — is human . . ."
24. Dodge
28. British farewell
31. Argentite, e.g.
32. Blossom part
34. Jolt
35. Departed
37. City pathway
39. Dawn goddess
41. Novelist Ferber
42. Gasped
45. More sizable
49. Secondary occupation
51. "The Thin Man" wife
52. The same: Latin
53. Conjunction
54. Emerald Isle: poetic
55. Sunday speeches: abbr.
56. Newspaper VIPs: abbr.
57. Bit of derring-do

DOWN

1. Queenly Hindu
2. Portentous sign
3. Singing Brothers
4. Furniture unit
5. Phrases in another way
6. New Haven collegian
7. Crazes
8. Declare
9. Indian prince, formerly
10. Matinee —, popular actor
11. Grackles
17. Summer: French
19. Speech defect
22. Bind (up) again
24. The sun
25. Anger
26. Protector
27. Canoeists, e.g.
29. Such: Spanish
30. Noah's craft
33. Ms. Horne
36. Clans' emblems
38. Alerted
40. Salt: French
42. Greek letters
43. Assistant
44. Enjoy an evening meal
46. Mr. Vidal
47. Cleveland's lake
48. Ayn or Sally
50. Go-ahead signal

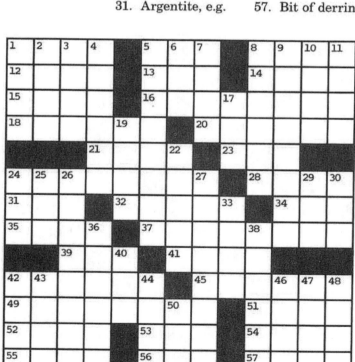

ACROSS

1. Ancient
4. Pine Tree State
9. Cold cubes
12. Ms. Farrow
13. Word with "tube" or "circle"
14. Distant
15. Whole
17. Capital of Austria
19. Instruct
20. Use an epee
21. Severity
23. Assist
26. Some salad dressings contain it
29. Cowboy show
30. Lyric poem
31. While
32. Thus
33. Prohibit (from)
34. Dallas native
36. Furiously destructive
38. Has lunch
39. Untidy
40. A finger or toe
42. Ensnares
46. "All —," conductor's cry
48. Country T.V. show: 2 wds.
49. Dove sound
50. Leering one
52. Actress Gardner
53. Paving substance
54. Has on
55. Wager

DOWN

1. Leave out
2. Long, thin mark
3. Computer input
4. Detroit is there
5. Industrious insect
6. At home
7. At no time
8. Ireland: poetic
9. Should it become necessary: 3 wds.
10. Is able
11. Notable time
16. Land measure
18. Reflected sound
20. In favor of
22. Car fuel
24. Thin
25. Harbor
26. Cast a ballot
27. Notion
28. In the adjacent house: hyph. wd.
29. Barnyard crowers
32. Family member, for short
35. Huge continent
36. Dog's M.D., for short
37. Harplike instrument
39. Tiny insect
41. Get bigger
43. Captain in "Moby Dick"
44. Cover with asphalt
45. Hard blow
46. Behave
47. Feather scarf
48. That woman
51. Scale note

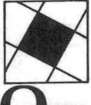

38

ACROSS

1. Present (a show)
6. Scribbles
13. Levied
14. Advance showing (of a film)
15. Leaves out
16. Retaliation
17. Indochinese country
18. Old sayings; proverbs
19. Golf "gizmo"
20. Common street name
21. Not that
22. Tenant's payment
23. In —, meeting (as a court)
25. Nuthatches and robins
26. Toward the stern
27. Shack
28. Group of employees
31. Overpowers with light
35. Unadulterated
36. Tease; heckle: slang
37. Cereal grain
38. Bobble a baseball, for example
39. Speeding penalty
40. Measure of land
41. Waking up
43. 747 or SST
44. An auto gear
45. Inn
46. Soft-shell clam
47. Gary Cooper film, "Mr. — Goes to Town"

DOWN

1. Fur scarves
2. Mexican dish
3. Self-evident truths
4. Understands (an idea)
5. Asner and Ames
6. Joint injury
7. Ships' workers
8. Guns (the motor)
9. Wide street: abbr.
10. Christmas season
11. Myth
12. Candy, cake, and cookies
18. Filmed
21. Spat
22. "Puttin' On the —"
24. Protected; secure
25. Bee's sound
27. Fog
28. Asparagus pieces
29. Small tower
30. Achieve fame and success
31. Warning sign word
32. Find
33. Part of ERA
34. Iron alloys
36. Remove soap from
39. Business company
40. Medicinal plant
42. Baltic or Caspian
43. Professor's degree: abbr.

ACROSS

1. Distinctive airs
6. Prefix with "American"
11. Froth
13. River of S.A.
14. Clincher: hyph. wd.
15. Do a secret agent's work, perhaps
16. With 39-Across, "Don't give up!": 3 wds.
18. And others: 2 wds. (abbr.)
21. Concepts
22. Victoria, and others
24. Common suffix
25. Theater sign: abbr.
28. Patient one
30. Glossy fabric
32. Hebrew letter
33. Holiday drink
35. Feature of a winding staircase
36. Preminger's 1944 classic
38. A Williams
39. See 16-Across: 3 wds.
43. "We — amused" (Queen Victoria): 2 wds.
44. Colorful
48. Economical types
49. Realtor's transaction
50. Cheats
51. Yo Yo Ma's instrument

DOWN

1. Devoured
2. Samovar
3. Disencumber
4. Was of use to
5. Sediment
6. "— with seven wives": 4 wds.
7. Tex-Mex fare
8. Black Sea arm
9. Rich source
10. Exceptional person
12. Jai —
13. "Gunsmoke" star
17. Mr. Amin
18. Dash
19. "No-no"
20. Related
23. Legislators
25. Basted
26. Oboe
27. Sole
29. Stirs
31. Garden hybrid: 2 wds.
34. 12 dozen: abbr.
36. Wedding gift, possibly
37. Declare openly
39. Russian news agency
40. Mideast country: variant
41. Jacob's son
42. Administrator: abbr.
45. Chess's Mikhail
46. Adverse
47. Corporate bigwig: abbr.

40

ACROSS

1. Fedora, for one
4. Disgrace
9. Parking area
12. Frost, as a cake
13. Decrease gradually
14. Have a debt
15. Balcony
17. In agreement: 2 wds.
19. Target
20. Without any changes: 2 wds.
21. Word with "under" and "T"
23. Make believe
26. Carry
27. Carnivals
28. Sink — swim
29. I am, you —, he is
30. Great joy
31. Gift for Dad
32. Exists
33. Signal light
34. Go by
35. Says again
37. Taxi riders
38. Girl
39. Airplane feature
40. Aside (from)
42. Professions
45. Sunbather's goal
46. Evade
48. Faucet
49. Before: poetic
50. Appointments
51. Pen for pigs

DOWN

1. Successful movie
2. King "beater"
3. White ant
4. Begin
5. Cut crudely
6. Gorilla, for one
7. Myself
8. Mistake removers
9. Unrestrained
10. Possess
11. Golf mound
16. Uncommon
18. Perches
20. Get up
21. Single step between floors
22. Equine
23. Couples
24. Clamor
25. Clothe
27. Deflated tires
30. Exploded
31. Goals
33. Terror
34. Window section
36. Carpenter's tool
37. Blazes
39. Walk in water
40. Consumed
41. Golf score
42. Use scissors
43. Large rodent
44. Secret agent
47. Creole State: abbr.

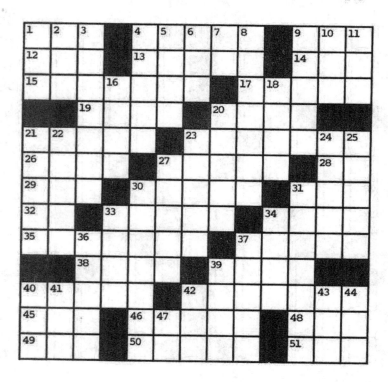

ACROSS

1. — -garde, forefront
6. Field mice
11. A detective, on occasion
12. Sarcastic
14. Block; hinder
15. Cuban leader
16. "— Indigo"
17. Mournful sound
19. Common street name
20. Make a gaffe
21. Gloomy
22. A woodwind
23. System of worship
24. Circuit; circumference
25. Historic Texas shrine
27. Dress up; primp
28. Part of a necklace
29. Horace or Thomas —
30. Italian coins
31. Sonny —, Cher's first husband
32. Possess
35. Doctor's group: abbr.
36. Jot
37. English elegy poet
38. Negligent
40. Wine vessel
42. Anode seekers
43. Small perforation
44. Irritable
45. Infuriate

DOWN

1. Mail, e.g.
2. Mist
3. Eagled a par three
4. Nancy Drew's boyfriend
5. Vibrato, in singing
6. A church officer
7. Algerian port
8. The: Spanish
9. Town on Lake Victoria
10. Choice menu item
11. Clock (a race)
13. Tailed celestial body
18. Word with "dug" or "time"
21. Dispose of
22. Augury
23. Etui, for one
24. Ligurian Sea tributary
25. Nourishment
26. Wyoming city
27. Cure-all
28. Barton, of the American Red Cross
29. Word: French
31. Domineering
32. Papal vestment worn over the alb
33. Eucharistic bread
34. No: Russian
36. Common contraction
37. Actor Peck, for short
39. Spotted American moths
41. Author Rand

hard

42

easy

ACROSS

1. Ocean
4. Strong wind
8. Thick slice
12. Rowing blade
13. In the center of
14. Employ
15. Had sleep visions
17. Polka or waltz
18. Ball-point item
19. Certain
20. Country byways
23. Handled the helm
26. Woe is me!
27. Kettles
28. Scale tone
29. Baby's napkin
30. Chick sounds
32. Received
33. All right
34. Went by car
35. Cod or Hatteras
36. Went on pension
38. Misplaces
39. Fair; just
40. Sandwich meat
41. Coal sources
43. Cattle herders
47. Aroma
48. Astronauts' goal
49. Tuition cost
50. "Star —"
51. Picnic pests
52. Overweight

DOWN

1. Turf
2. Corn spike
3. "You — the Sunshine of My Life"
4. Chess, etc.
5. Prayer-ending word
6. Jar cover
7. Actor Asner
8. "Divvies" (with others)
9. Ocean —, passenger ship
10. Curved line
11. "Busy" insect
16. Mimics
17. Songs for two
19. Halt!
20. Work hard
21. The same
22. Seize suddenly
23. Velocity
24. Wed secretly
25. Engagements
30. Reads (over) carefully
31. Biblical garden
32. Car fuel
34. Danube, Nile, etc.
35. Search thoroughly
37. Pavarotti's voice
38. Grass-covered yards
40. Owl's cry
41. Cut the grass
42. "Apple cider" girl of song
43. Pro and —
44. Light-switch word
45. Opposite of "nay"
46. Fix (a time)
48. Pa's mate

ACROSS

1. Assistance
4. Prayer ending
8. Noisy quarrel
12. Enemy
13. No part
14. Highway strip
15. Wonder
16. Deity
17. Advertises, as a reward
18. Sword
20. Dinner course
21. Maid
23. Canadian province: abbr.
25. Make no — about, admit freely
28. Fold-up bed
29. Mr. Durocher
30. Notable ages
31. Farm animal
32. Army vehicle
33. Deposit
34. Jolt; shock
35. Windy
36. Mr. Capone
37. Streamers
39. Baronet's wife
40. Spunk
44. Library property
46. Health resort
47. Unprocessed
48. Otherwise
49. Favorites
50. Presidential nickname
51. Caribou
52. Comedy's Martha
53. Part of MPH

DOWN

1. At a distance
2. Hawkeye State
3. Profound
4. California team
5. Melba, of song
6. Outcome
7. Compass point
8. Baker's need
9. Grate
10. Social insect
11. Absolutely!
17. Keats, for one
19. Frosts
20. Weather forecast, perhaps
22. Squirrel's find
23. Borsch vegetable
24. Mimic
25. Lugosi, of film
26. College exam
27. Certain vote
29. French article
31. Chaplin prop
32. Fair
34. Becomes wedged
35. Lubricant
37. Pastry chef
38. Vacant
39. Prescribed amount
41. Stumble
42. Superior or Erie
43. Pitcher
44. River bottom
45. Spanish cheer
46. Vast amount
49. San Juan's island: abbr.

43

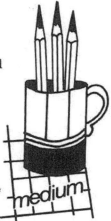

medium

44

ACROSS

1. Breathed laboriously
7. Cooper's product
13. Ballpark referee
14. Orange-and-black bird
15. Bowling scores
16. Small streams
17. Sour substance
19. Baseball great, Mel —
20. Ms. Ekland
23. Light beams
25. Madrid's language: abbr.
27. Uncouth
28. — wrestling, Japanese sport
29. One of journalism's "five W's"
30. Wholly
31. Domesticates
32. Possesses
33. Born
34. Song of praise
35. Intimidates
36. Physician: abbr.
37. Sagacious
38. Ladd western
39. Exclamations
40. Garden tool
42. Dodgers' old home, — Field
45. Christmas Eve flyer
49. Scarab, e.g.
50. Clothing
51. Floppy-eared hound
52. Botched (up)

DOWN

1. Virgil Grissom's nickname
2. Electrical unit
3. Resort
4. Publish without permission
5. Construct
6. Mr. Arnaz
7. Actor Hoskins
8. Gullies
9. Tumults
10. Core
11. Wapiti
12. Bandleader Brown
18. Krupa or Rich
20. Trademark
21. Czar or shah
22. Not in use
24. Prayer ending
25. Comedian, Dick —
26. Sheriff's group
28. Utters
29. Command to Trigger
31. Prickly plant
35. Storage boxes
37. Sharpens
38. Emulate Dorothy Hamill
39. Vigoda and Lincoln
41. Name in a famous palindrome
42. Lessen
43. Actress Arthur
44. Tennis division
46. Towel word, sometimes
47. Poet's "before"
48. Artist Grooms

ACROSS

1. Church seat
4. Nourished
7. Yarns
9. Ethical
11. Eloquent speaker
13. Captain Kidd, for one
14. Gross minus expenses
15. Walked in water
17. Tennis match unit
18. Morning moisture
20. Sailor
21. "Angry" color
22. 24 hours
24. Subtraction word
26. Obtain
28. Boy
29. Incentive pay
31. Puppy, for one
33. Beachgoer's goal
34. Old horse
36. Knock sharply
38. Move swiftly
39. Foot lever
41. Arrest
43. Wanes
45. Unmarried
47. Mansion with property
48. Portioned (out)
49. Plant fluid
50. Marry

DOWN

1. Peeled
2. Overjoyed
3. Soggy
4. In favor of
5. Rubs out a mistake
6. Saw socially
7. 2000 lbs.
8. Female hog
9. Among: poetic
10. Allow
12. Rodent
13. Danger
16. Water barrier
19. Cart
21. More impolite
23. Fanciful desire
25. Siesta
27. Melodies
29. Monkey's delight
30. Unhappy
32. Snarl
33. Huge brass instruments
35. Car fuel
37. Became wan
38. Male sheep
39. For each
40. Cover
42. A four-poster is one kind
44. Spinning toy
46. At this time

46

ACROSS

1. Motorist's chart
4. Farm implement
8. To —, exactly: 2 wds.
12. Mistake
13. Miss Horne
14. Auctioned off
15. Adolescent
17. Misplace
18. Ballpoints
19. Miss Hayes
20. Pursue
22. Footwear item
24. Injure
25. Run off suddenly, as frightened cattle
29. Spanish cheer
30. Grin
31. Deposit (eggs)
32. Traveler's document
34. At this place
35. Hauls
36. Peace symbols
37. Prize
40. Region
41. Sit for a portrait
42. Forefather
46. A Great Lake
47. Red planet
48. Historical period
49. Transmitted
50. Grows older
51. Harden, as cement

DOWN

1. Encountered
2. Exist
3. Gets ready
4. Aircraft
5. Lower limbs
6. Half a pair
7. Armed conflict
8. Napping
9. Hammer or wrench
10. Otherwise
11. Paradise
16. Bird shelter
19. Residence
20. Use an ax
21. Hawaiian dance
22. Moves slightly
23. Stop
25. Smoke and fog
26. Raises
27. Challenge
28. Watches closely
30. Potato
33. Avenue
34. Weeding tools
36. Woman's garment
37. Mimics
38. Had on
39. "It's — to tell a lie": 2 wds.
40. Land measure
42. Doctors' group: abbr.
43. Henpeck
44. Raw metal
45. Rodent

easy

ACROSS

1. Cereal grain
4. Successful songs
8. Rugged rock
12. Malt beverage
13. Notion
14. Nevada city
15. Famous gorilla: 2 wds.
17. Writer Ferber
18. Fight (of honor)
19. Painter's stand
20. Popular game
22. Olive seeds
24. Injure
25. Round Table knight
29. Total amount
30. Troop's movement
31. Conceit
32. Pilgrim settlement
34. Assembly room
35. Actor Griffith
36. Drive back
37. Metallic sound
40. Cautious
41. Trumpet, for one
42. Idle person: slang
46. A Great Lake
47. Actress Chase
48. Fruit drink
49. Have on
50. Boat dock
51. "Twilight Zone"'s Serling

DOWN

1. Sturdy tree
2. — Baba
3. Affectionately
4. Long walks
5. Golden Calf, for one
6. "X," numerically
7. Droop
8. Wrinkle
9. Beatty movie
10. Actress Baxter
11. Aim
16. Rush (of wind)
19. Engrave
20. English "fellow"
21. Frame of a ship
22. Shindig
23. Measure of length
25. Praise
26. When February 29th occurs: 2 wds.
27. Make eyes (at)
28. Turnpike charge
30. Friar
33. Way; method
34. Bandleader Alpert
36. Speeder detector
37. Masticate
38. Traditional knowledge
39. Opera solo
40. Rouse
42. Brief swim
43. Actor Wallach
44. Commotion
45. Actor Knight

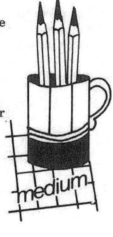

48 BIBLE CROSSWORD MEDIUM

by MARILYN WING

Bible references in this puzzle are from the King James Version. You'll find it stimulating to solve, and may discover you know more about the Bible than you think you do.

ACROSS

1. — day long I have stretched forth my hands. *Rom. 10:21*
4. Withhold not good from them to — it is due. *Prov. 3:27*
8. David arose from off his —. *II Sam. 11:2*
11. As thou hast —, so must we do. *Ezra 10:12*
13. — a little, and there a little. *Isa. 28:10*
14. Jehu r— in a chariot. *II Ki. 9:16*
15. What is — than honey? *Judg. 14:18*
17. A king shall — over us. *I Sam. 12:12*
19. Who ... — be compared unto the Lord? *Ps. 89:6*
20. Whatsoever hath fins and —, ... them shall ye eat. *Lev. 11:9*
21. With their — toward the temple ... and their faces toward the east. *Ezek. 8:16*
24. The streets ... shall be full of — and girls. *Zech. 8:5*
25. Thou, Lord, art high —ve all the earth. *Ps. 97:9*
26. Then shall ye — that I am he. *St. John 8:28*
28. So is thy praise unto the — of the earth. *Ps. 48:10*
32. Against him that bendeth let the archer — his bow. *Jer. 51:3*
34. Two are better than —. *Eccles. 4:9*
35. I did cast them out as the — in the streets. *Ps. 18:42*
36. I am the Lord and there is none —. *Isa. 45:5*
37. No man can serve two mas—. *Matt. 6:24*
39. The kings of the north, far and —r ... shall drink. *Jer. 25:26*

40. Two hundred —, and twenty rams. *Gen. 32:14*
42. Her light was ... — as crystal. *Rev. 21:11*
44. They were thy merchants: they — in thy market. *Ezek. 27:17*
47. He —d the fare thereof. *Jonah 1:3*
48. Ye come together not for the better, but for the —. *I Cor. 11:17*
49. Children, obey your —. *Eph. 6:1*
53. — (2 words) what I am. *I. Cor. 15:10*
54. Some of them ye shall — and crucify. *Matt. 23:34*
56. They were — afraid. *Luke 2:9*
57. Give ear unto my voice, when I — unto thee. *Ps. 141:1*
58. There shall come ... a rod out of the — of Jesse. *Isa. 11:1*
59. — is me! for I am undone. *Isa. 6:5*

DOWN

1. Thine ox and thine — may rest. *Ex. 23:12*
2. The — of Moses should not be broken. *St. John 7:23*
3. They — in wait for my soul. *Ps. 59:3*
4. — wilt thou return? *Neh. 2:6*
5. She brought forth — first-born son. *Luke 2:7*
6. Take ... one — two. *Matt. 18:16*
7. Jesus, Master, have — on us. *Luke 17:13*
8. The fire causeth the waters to —. *Isa. 64: 2*
9. The children's teeth are set on —. *Jer. 31:29*
10. The beasts go into — and remain. *Job 37:8*

12. — thyself now with majesty . . . and array thyself with glory. *Job 40:10*
16. Fulfil your works, your daily —s. *Ex. 5:13*
18. I mean not that other men be —, and ye burdened. *II Cor. 8:13*
20. A — went forth to sow. *Matt. 13:3*
21. Ye shall find the — . . . lying in a manger. *Luke 2:12*
22. Cain and —
23. This great fire will —ume us. *Deut. 5:25*
24. A spirit hath not flesh and —. *Luke 24:39*
27. I will shew thee that which is — in the scripture. *Dan. 10:21*
29. They came . . . at the end of — months. *II Sam. 24:8*
30. Your old men shall —m dreams. *Joel 2:28*
31. We have seen his — in the east. *Matt. 2:2*
33. Worthy — are done unto this nation. *Acts 24:2*

38. The woman was arrayed in purple and —let. *Rev. 17:4*
41. Daniel was mourning three full —. *Dan. 10:2*
43. A false witness will utter —. *Prov. 14:5*
44. God speaketh once, yea —e. *Job 33:14*
45. They shall — like young lions. *Isa. 5:29*
46. The Philistines had put . . . — against army. *I Sam. 17:21*
47. He . . . struck Jesus with the — of his hand. *St. John 18:22*
49. The Lord is in his holy tem—. *Ps. 11:4*
50. Now ye are full, — ye are rich. *I Cor. 4:8*
51. The Philistines were gathered . . . into a —op. *II Sam. 23:11*
52. Having eyes, — ye not? *Mark 8:18*
55. — is finished. *St. John 19:30*

57

49

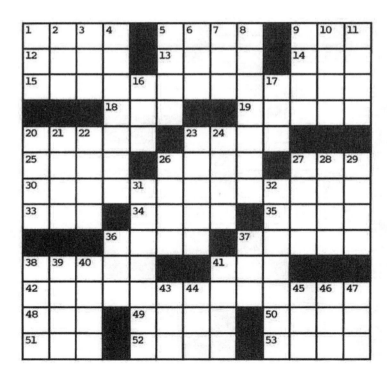

ACROSS

1. Ram's feature
5. Famous chanteuse
9. Smidgen
12. Healing plant
13. Crazy: slang
14. "Born in the —," rock hit
15. College football prize: 2 wds.
18. Foil material
19. Fencing weapons
20. Relieve
23. Party thrower
25. Of sound body
26. Famous film plantation
27. Casino cube
30. Motion-picture presentations: 2 wds.
33. Scandinavian country: abbr.
34. Flake, as paint
35. Pairs
36. Lane targets
37. Walk slowly
38. Ancient Greek city
41. "The Greatest"
42. Writing honor: 2 wds.
48. Haggard novel
49. Body of learning
50. Yemeni capital
51. Part of a famous palindrome
52. Long time periods
53. Touch down

DOWN

1. Triumphant exclamation
2. *Corrida* cry: Spanish
3. Louis XIV, for one: French
4. Snuggled
5. Blueprint
6. Charged atom
7. — up, misbehave
8. Anticipated
9. Cat's-paw
10. U.S. Davis Cup coach
11. Inlets
16. Wire measure
17. Not required: abbr.
20. Food fish
21. Movement rate
22. Verve
23. 19th U.S. President
24. Spoken
26. "Feds": hyph. wd.
27. Cudgel
28. Object of worship
29. Being: Latin
31. New Testament letter
32. Naval officer
36. Hawaiian alimentary paste
37. Swiss mountain
38. Church part
39. West German industrial area
40. Joy
41. A son of Zeus
43. Menagerie
44. Sea eagle
45. Cretan peak
46. Buddhist sect
47. Purpose

ACROSS

1. Not well-lit
4. Coin openings
9. Obese
12. High card
13. Plane driver
14. Belonging to us
15. Affirmative reply
16. Strange
17. Unaccompanied
19. Uses a chair
21. Attractive
22. Celebrities
24. Dines
25. Very large
26. Walking sticks
27. Laughter sound
29. Mine product
30. Confined, as a bird
31. Soft drink
32. Atop
33. Jabs
34. Instance
35. Above
36. Organs of smell
37. Glows
40. Jumps like a rabbit
41. Broader
42. Crude cabin
43. Malt beverage
46. Fruit drink
47. Rub out
49. Merry
50. Pod vegetable
51. Writing tables
52. Female sheep

DOWN

1. Actress, Doris —
2. Frozen water
3. Communication
4. Specks
5. Container tops
6. Not new
7. Toward
8. Began
9. Twelve inches
10. Uncle's wife
11. A three-spot card
18. Not as much
20. Anger
21. Window glasses
22. Scat!
23. Rotate
24. Avid
26. Bakery items
27. Stockings
28. Large monkeys
30. Concealed; wrapped
31. Corridor
33. Cornbread
34. Policeman
36. Memorandums
37. Exchange
38. — and seek
39. Thought
40. Corn covering
42. Owns
44. Statute
45. Organ of sight
48. Concerning

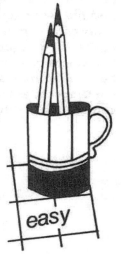

easy

Puzzles 51 and 52 have been started for you to give you your initial clues. Use both the definitions and the definition numbers as aids in supplying the words and the black squares to go into the diagram. Remember, the pattern of black squares is symmetrical. The example below shows the meaning of symmetry of the black squares in the diagram. When you have discovered the correct placement of a black square, its mate can be inserted in a corresponding position on the opposite side of the diagram. If you are still having difficulty solving Diagramless puzzles, see opposite page for information about a leaflet you can send for. Starting boxes for the other puzzles are listed on the last page.

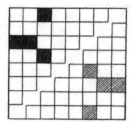

ACROSS

1. Hula-hoop was one
4. Theater platform
9. Pod vegetable
12. Frozen water
13. Child's four-wheeler
14. Everything
15. — off, begin a golf game
16. Large monkey
17. Brittle, as celery
19. Window glass
21. Playground fixtures
22. Toboggans
24. Quit
25. Stockings
26. Group of students
27. "— it ever so humble . . ."
29. Grain morsel
30. Portion
31. Chum
32. — course, certainly
33. Skirt vents
34. Peaceful
35. Easy canter
36. Flowers popular on Valentine's Day
37. Soda sippers
40. Hair ribbons
41. Inscribed
42. Naughty
43. Sum up
46. Point (a finger) at
47. Polish, as shoes
49. Merry
50. Spinning toy
51. Latin dance
52. Spud bud

DOWN

1. Temper tantrum
2. High playing card
3. Most low, as a voice
4. Graceful, long-necked water birds
5. Record on cassette
6. Sweet sixteen, for one
7. Leave
8. Surround
9. Settled a bill
10. Otherwise
11. Swiss mountains
18. Tears (apart)
20. Fruit-juice drink
21. Plays the leading role
22. Begone, chickens!

23. Bread shape
24. Blackboard material
26. Dish defects
27. Hay bundle
28. Shade trees
30. Most sluggish

31. Film, "A — to India"
33. Bed plank
34. Dairy animal
36. Broncobusting show
37. Wallop (a housefly)

38. Threesome
39. Frolic (about)
40. Slam (a door)
42. Box for coal
44. 24 hours
45. Easter-egg coloring
48. Laughter sound

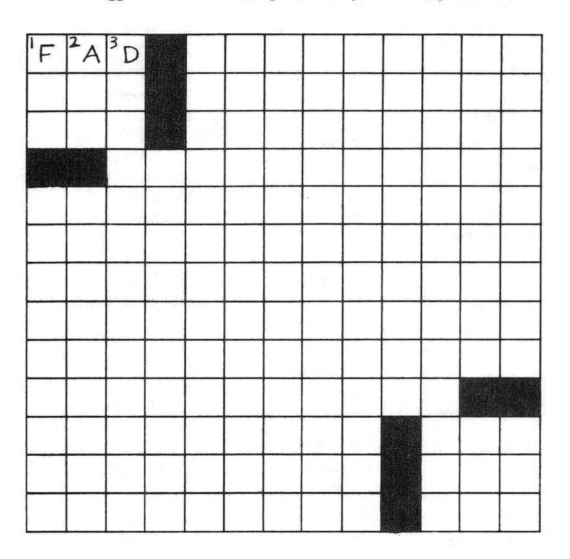

This Diagramless is 15 boxes wide by 15 boxes deep.

ACROSS

1. Slice
4. Knight's title
7. Quality of sound
8. Equine gait
10. Rank; rate
11. Mechanical man
13. Blackboard
14. Transgression
15. Energy
17. Burden
18. Stony
20. Dog's foot
22. More mature
24. Fawn's mother
25. Steeple top
27. Great grief
28. Once again
30. Kept from the sun
31. Binds
32. Portal
33. Meal
36. Created
37. Mouth part
40. Worship
41. Bad actor: slang
42. Seasoning
44. Nothing
45. Speech impediments
47. Prayer ending
48. Five pairs
50. Inquire
51. VCR recordings
53. Indications
55. Small bays
56. Step
57. Above
58. Four-poster
59. For each

DOWN

1. Outer garment
2. Beneath
3. Golf peg
4. Hit
5. Sarcasm; satire
6. Actor Reiner
7. Exchange
9. Spinning toy
10. Forest meadow
12. Lukewarm
13. Perform alone
14. Barge
16. Peel
17. Deep
19. Lyric poems
21. Marry
23. Lift
25. Loafers and pumps
26. Average
29. Tennis-court feature
30. Turf
31. Paving substance
32. Moist
33. Moved swiftly
34. Prepare for publication
35. Fishing rods
36. "Lone Ranger's" disguise
37. Green citrus fruits
38. Frosts (a cake)
39. Animal enclosure
41. Made snake sounds
43. Writing material
45. Spear
46. Kitchen range
49. Bite; pinch
52. Affirm
54. Chatter
55. Policeman: slang

53 MOVIE-TV CROSSWORD

by Myrtle Bazemore

ACROSS

1. Actress Gabor
4. Marsh
9. Snares
14. Intention
15. Country-music star Tucker
16. *Grand —*, Greta Garbo movie
17. Actor Burr
19. Movie, *Charlie — in Egypt*
21. *— Kill a Mockingbird*, Gregory Peck movie
22. *— of the Past*, Robert Mitchum film
23. MGM's Leo, for one
24. Vigor
25. Separately
28. Magician's aid
29. Be concerned
30. Washbasin
31. Sonny —, Cher's former partner
32. 1977 movie, *A Bridge Too —*
33. Singer, — "King" Cole
34. Singer Falana
35. Affectionate touch
38. Printer's measure
39. *Cat on a Hot Tin —*
40. Entertainer, Tennessee Ernie —
41. Singing syllable
42. Mr. Redford
44. Unfurnished
45. Swindle: slang
46. Comedian Buttons
47. Actor Van Dyke
48. State of mind
49. Ginger's dancing partner
51. 5,280 feet
52. TV's *— Days*
53. Not high
54. *Kiss and —*, Shirley Temple movie
55. *Wheel of Fortune* host Sajak
56. *I — the Law*, Edward G. Robinson movie
57. *— the End of Time*, Robert Mitchum film

58. Actress, Shelley —
62. Marsha —, star of *The Goodbye Girl*
64. Family name on TV's *Dallas*
66. Sheep's cry
67. Robert Mitchum picture, *The — Below*
68. Leases
69. *—-Hur*, 1959 Charlton Heston classic

DOWN

1. Hearing organ
2. By way of
3. *Little Women* character
4. Plump
5. Desire
6. *Smokey — the Bandit*, Burt Reynolds movie
7. Rex Harrison movie, *— Fair Lady*
8. Actor, Al —
9. "Younger — Springtime," song from *South Pacific*
10. — Howard, Richie of 52-Across
11. *— the Circus*, Marx Brothers movie
12. Henry Fonda's son
13. Incline
18. Onetime TV role for Robin Williams
20. Coal scuttle
23. Actress Turner
24. Peel
25. Ed —, TV's Lou Grant
26. Liberace's instrument
27. Picnic pest
28. Edward G. Robinson movie, *The Sea —*
29. *— Sharks*, game show
31. *Das —*, 1981 West German film
32. Price of passage
34. *Little — Fauntleroy*, Mickey Rooney movie
35. Bottle stopper
36. Single-masted sailboat

37. Actress Duncan
39. Film critic, Rex —
40. TV show, — *the Nation*
43. Prepare, as coffee
44. Mr. Cosby
45. Policeman
47. Comedienne, Phyllis —
48. — Houston, TV detective
49. Blaze
50. Director Polanski
51. Chili-maker on TV's *Alice*
52. Suspends

54. Entertainer, — Tim
55. Liquid measure
57. Actor Selleck
58. Score a victory
59. Recede, as the tide
60. Charlotte —, Mrs. Garrett on TV's *The Facts of Life*
61. *The Streets of — Francisco*, TV show
63. Compass point
65. *The Way — Were*, 1973 Barbra Streisand movie

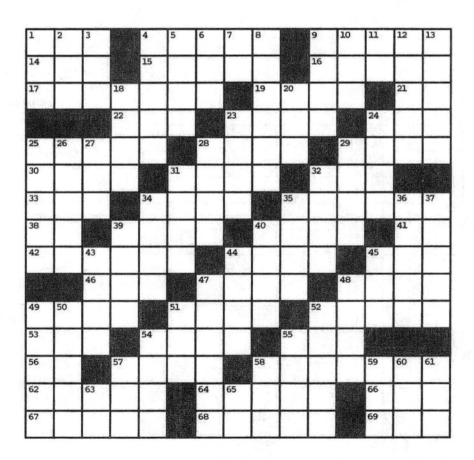

54

ACROSS

1. Mock
5. Converse informally
9. For each
12. Fairy-tale monster
13. Simple
14. Fuss
15. Bread-browning device
17. Danger
19. Body of water
20. Not public
22. Streaks
25. Got a hole in one
26. Spar
27. Food fish
29. Recede, as the tide
32. "The Wizard of —"
33. Glitter
36. Either
37. Obtain
39. Straight pencil mark
40. Golf cry
42. Lion's sound
44. Give back (money)
46. Purify
49. Spoil
50. Word with "beat" or "felt"
51. Rises in anger: 2 wds.
55. Dine
56. Building wings
58. Girl's name
59. Seven-day periods: abbr.
60. Female deer
61. Printer's word

DOWN

1. — down, make a note of
2. Self
3. Rubs out
4. Reperforms an usher's job
5. Letter following bee
6. Angel's musical instrument
7. While
8. Characteristic
9. Procession
10. Revise, as a manuscript
11. Actor's part
16. Sailor
18. Night before a holiday
21. More rancid
22. L.A.'s atmospheric woe
23. Labyrinth
24. Series of steps
28. Large metal container
30. Nee
31. Raised, as dogs
34. Seeded
35. Attempts
38. Pays for another's food
41. Beginning
43. Paddle
45. Historical period
46. Masticate
47. Certain disclosure
48. Writer Gardner
52. Curvy letter
53. Employ
54. Attention-getting sound
57. "— and behold"

55

Easy

ACROSS

1. Large, stringed instrument
5. Not at work
8. Oyster's kin
12. Above
13. Dove's call
14. Country road
15. Walk in water
16. Window en-hancers
18. Goad (on)
20. Ferris wheel, etc.
21. Nearer
24. Not speaking
25. Black bird
26. Crusted des-sert
27. Hole in a fence
30. Refrigerated
31. Owned
32. Identical
33. Vereen or Hogan
34. Light-brown color
35. Parking timer
36. Water barrier
37. Soften in temper; yield
38. Watch band
41. Location
42. Defends
44. Bit of film
48. Relieve (a pain)
49. Sturdy tree
50. Grow weary
51. Colors, as hair
52. Snoop (into)
53. Petty quarrel

DOWN

1. In what way?
2. Actress Gard-ner
3. Bright color
4. Ironed, as clothes
5. Take place
6. — -poster, bed-stead
7. In favor of
8. Title, as for land
9. — aside, saved
10. Actress Meara
11. Untidy state
17. Factual
19. Ball-point item
21. Bed for baby
22. Shoestring
23. Microwave unit
24. Center: abbr.
26. Skillet
27. Fence door
28. Prayer-ending word
29. Lively and cute
31. Sandwich meat
32. Chooses
34. Adhesive strip
35. N.Y.C. base-baller
36. Engagements
37. Chancy
38. Drove too fast
39. Serving platter
40. Corsage flower
41. Movie, "A — Is Born"
43. Policeman
45. Insolent talk: slang
46. A Gershwin
47. Favorite

ACROSS

1. Swaps
7. Brownish-yellow
12. Go to bed
13. Pants; gasps
15. "I think, therefore I —."
16. Half-quart
18. Place for a bracelet
19. Swindle: slang
21. Revise (a manuscript)
23. "Sad" color
24. Always
26. Stain
28. New England State: abbr.
29. Did a tailor's job
31. Reel
34. Corn spikes
36. Play the leading role
37. More vigorous
40. Freezing rain
43. Mr. Jolson
44. Pare
46. Roof edge
47. Tumult
50. Chair
52. Apex
53. Danger
55. Trail
57. Football position: abbr.
58. Entraps
60. Mourn; lament
62. Toboggans
63. Birds of the falcon family

DOWN

1. Tiny amounts
2. Eliminate
3. By
4. Food offering at parties
5. A New York canal
6. Dispatches
7. Exclamation of delight
8. Make a cat's sound
9. Cutting remark
10. Wicked
11. Pick up
14. Use a rudder
17. Gratuities
20. Less worn
22. Small children
25. Register, as a thermometer
27. Makes lace
30. Leak, as a faucet
32. Strong wind
33. Terrific!
35. Looks at
37. Angels' instruments
38. Outsiders; strangers
39. Clarinet, for one
41. Develop gradually
42. Indian tents
45. Very big
48. Type of exam
49. Grow weary
51. "Gone With the Wind" plantation
54. Caused
56. Band's engagement
59. Baseball infielder: abbr.
61. Overhead train

Medium

57

Hard

ACROSS

1. Adder
4. Move slightly
8. At a distance: poetic
12. Sticky stuff: slang
13. Walking stick
14. Stratagem
15. Refrains (from)
17. Sleeves
18. Like the Empire State Building
19. Menace
21. Suggest
23. Loyal
24. Small recess
25. Timidity
26. Bird of prey
29. Weight unit
30. Track
31. By way of
32. Pindaric work
33. Brass-wind instrument
34. Torn
35. Fail to attain
36. Morgan or Clydesdale
37. Give help to
40. Indigent
41. Head: slang
42. "Put the finger on"
46. "— me your ears . . ."
47. Number on a baseball team
48. Female eland
49. — out, makes (a living)
50. Acquires
51. Notable age

DOWN

1. Turkish leader
2. Weep
3. Defer
4. Like a fish
5. Part of a comet
6. Tavern
7. Curb; check
8. Conscious (of)
9. Inferno
10. Soprano Gluck
11. Repose
16. Speak
20. Throw with force
21. Division word
22. State of mind
23. Lachrymations
25. Icing
26. Disregard
27. Takes the gold
28. Tardy
30. The thing mentioned
34. Word with "beer" or "cellar"
35. Heeds
36. Whetstones
37. Competent
38. Go in search of
39. Rational
40. Confined (with "up")
43. Fade away
44. In favor of
45. Affirmative vote

ACROSS

1. Sunbeam
4. Cry of triumph
7. Stubborn ones
9. Head part
11. Mexican dish
12. Assistant
14. Sphere
15. Large ponds
17. A Gershwin
18. Singer Torme
19. Pot cover
20. Bite; pinch
21. Perceived
24. Cain's brother
26. Help
27. Pub order
28. Golf stroke
30. Shrink from; cower
33. Prohibit
34. Dying vessel
35. Cereal grain
37. Picnic pest
38. Outdoor lounging area
40. Snaky fish
41. Worships
43. Swords
45. By oneself
46. Fast gaits
47. — Moines, Iowa
48. Distress signal

DOWN

1. Thunder sound
2. — carte: 2 wds.
3. Shout
4. Top cards
5. Actor Linden
6. Of high mountains
7. Female horses
8. Closed tightly
9. Outbuilding
10. Danger
11. Male turkey
13. Knock
16. Young goat
22. Late singer, — King Cole
23. Use a chair
24. Famed boxer
25. Mr. Gazzara
27. Sculptor, for one
28. Chinese bear
29. Not revealed
30. Feline
31. Welcomes
32. Oglers
33. Sheep bleat
34. Flower holder
36. Overhead trains
38. Writing tools
39. Paddles
42. Fish eggs
44. Ghostly cry

Medium

59

ACROSS

1. Boy
4. Thanksgiving dinner, for example
9. Health resort
12. Eden dweller
13. Mistake
14. Baseball player's hat
15. Opening
16. Mouse's "cousin"
17. Idolize
19. Has
21. Tennis and polo
22. Eyeglass holders
24. Word before "sugar" or "syrup"
25. Leave out
26. Wall section

27. One-third of a yard: abbr.
29. Allow
30. Made bread
31. M.D.'s charge
32. "— apple a day"
33. Marathon entrant
34. Ladd or Alda
35. Spud, to some
36. Sound from an angry bull
37. Begins
39. Choir voice
40. Desert beast
41. Mine find
42. Water barrier
45. Pub brew
46. Finished
48. Conceit
49. Crimson
50. Fountain drinks

51. Morning droplets

DOWN

1. Table part
2. Actress Gardner
3. Kind of bank transaction
4. Plants for hanging baskets
5. Notable ages
6. Painting or sculpture
7. Very
8. Caught (in a snare)
9. Make a T.D.
10. Play role
11. Chimps, for example
18. Barbie or Raggedy Ann
20. Moist
21. More rational
22. Soft drink favorite
23. So be it!
24. Creator
26. Steps
27. Terror
28. Camper's shelter, perhaps
30. Fights
31. Overflowed
33. Unusual
34. Hill-dwelling insect
35. Domesticated
36. Toboggans and others
37. Healed wound mark
38. Story
39. Region
41. Strange
43. Grow older
44. Cut (a lawn)
47. Negative reply

Easy

JUMBO CROSSWORD

EASY

ACROSS

1. Ancient
4. Prolonged look
9. Flip (a coin)
13. Coffee's rival
14. Detroit baseballer
15. Sports palace
17. Light brown
18. Run off to wed
19. Blossom segment
20. Flee
22. Muscle complaint
24. Bind
25. Actress Donna, and family
26. Nibble
27. Woes
28. Roadside eateries
30. Lyric poem
31. Mimic
34. Adjusts (a clock)
35. Throbs
38. Is akin (to)
40. Unusual
41. Suffice
42. Swapped
43. Fasteners
44. Kennedy or Knight
45. Asphalting
46. Hurl; toss
47. Salad fish
48. Flower stalk
50. Hatteras or Cod
51. Funnyman Rickles
52. Boy
53. Peel
54. Take to jail
57. Actor Pacino
58. Film-studio worker
60. Behold!
61. Act properly
63. Plane personnel
64. Payable
65. Washington bill
66. Blueprint
67. Pleads
68. High wind
70. Baby's bed
71. Tic-——-toe
72. Spanish "rah"
73. Laundering need
74. Buccaneer
77. While
78. Sacred
79. Acrobat; gymnast
80. In the direction of
82. Shoe bottom
83. Baltic or Bering
84. Exist
85. Corn stems
87. Tardy
89. Burden
90. Noblemen
94. Reverent wonder
95. Shopping wagon
96. Say over and over
97. Actress Thomas
99. Holland bloom
101. High card
102. Staff of life
103. Wear away slowly
104. Passing grade
105. Rim
106. Prevent
107. Recipe abbr.

DOWN

1. Playful aquatic
2. Rental document
3. Waltz or polka
4. "Cinderella" meanie
5. Flooring square
6. In the past
7. Fixes
8. Builds
9. Adhesive strip
10. Unrefined metal
11. Colonizes
12. Slow-moving mollusk
16. Beerlike drinks
21. Sum up
23. That boy
26. Wagers
27. Unemployed
29. Want
30. Yours and mine
31. Actor Carney
32. For each
33. Filled with joy
35. Huff and puff
36. Biblical garden
37. Fountain order
39. Eve's mate
40. Ascend
43. Staple's kin: 2 wds.
44. Melody
46. Custody
47. Ripped
48. Thick slice
49. Story
50. Arrived
51. Sketch
53. Surface (a road)
54. Prayer ending
55. Hit hard
56. Foot digits
58. Walking aid
59. Desert wanderer
62. Cavity
64. Wall stickers
66. Say grace
67. Cutting remark
68. Bewhiskered animal
69. In addition
70. Icy
71. Sports official
73. Painful to touch
74. Tug
75. Kickoff gadget
76. Historical time
78. Jack rabbit
79. Froglike animal
81. Sprinkled (the lawn)
82. One's natural height
85. Separated, as laundry
86. Tree fluid
87. Baby sheep
88. Conscious (of)
89. Scale tone
91. Respond (to)
92. Shoestrings
93. Sharply inclined
95. Morse system
96. Emulate a jockey
98. Fall behind
100. Car-park area

61

Medium

ACROSS

1. Jewel
4. Speed contest
8. Jazz composer Waller, familiarly
12. Ms. Gardner
13. False god
14. Part of a monogram: abbr.
15. Choir member
17. Sicilian volcano
18. — of March, bad day for Caesar
19. Conceit
21. Window parts
23. Ace of clubs, for one
24. Region
25. French artist and family
29. Each
30. Recorded
31. Dine
32. Evaluated
34. Musician Brubeck
35. Large tubs
36. Attack
37. Aim; seek
40. Farm structure
41. Diving bird
42. Lounge chair
46. Actor Guinness
47. And others: 2 wds. (abbr.)
48. Before: poetic
49. Short letter
50. Rather and Dailey
51. Mom's mate

DOWN

1. Chat
2. A Gabor
3. Seamen
4. Ceremonies
5. Stirs
6. Cheat: slang
7. Raised
8. Devilish people
9. Against: prefix
10. Dye
11. Remain
16. Notion
20. Like the Sahara
21. Father
22. Greek god of war
23. Cod and Canaveral
25. Conquered
26. Salted
27. Roof projection
28. Printer's term
30. Russian ruler
33. Make evident
34. Certain food shop, for short
36. Beaks
37. Alda of M*A*S*H
38. Fly alone
39. Bard
40. Look over quickly
43. Greek letter
44. Epoch
45. Bright color

ACROSS

1. In what manner?
4. Not good
7. Decompose
10. Prayer ending
12. Falsehood
13. Take a bus
14. Become bored (of)
15. State further
16. Atop
17. Trials
19. Beneath
21. Small child
22. Pool stick
23. More unfavorable
26. Take back
30. Exist
31. Cover
32. Firearm
33. Made less
36. Slumbered
38. In no manner
39. A certain thing
40. Swoon
42. Valentine symbol
45. Grain storage structure
46. Utilize
48. College official
50. Actor Alda
51. Automobile
52. Store event
53. Of course!
54. Female sheep
55. Favorite

DOWN

1. Bonnet
2. Leave out
3. Used to be
4. Explosion
5. Assist
6. Reasoned out
7. Ready to be picked
8. Aroma
9. Five pairs
11. Birds' homes
13. More impolite
18. Foot digit
20. Pecan, for one
23. Armed conflict
24. Metallic rock
25. Bright color
26. Free (from)
27. Grow older
28. Coffee container
29. Used in 4-Down: abbr.
31. Salad ingredient
34. Labor organization
35. Against
36. That woman
37. Guides
39. At that place
40. Office record
41. Cry of dismay
43. Harvest
44. Yarn; story
45. Speak
47. Carpenter's tool
49. Mesh trap

Easy

63 BIBLE CROSSWORD MEDIUM

by MARILYN WING

Bible references in this puzzle are from the King James Version. You'll find it stimulating to solve, and may discover you know more Bible than you think you do.

ACROSS

1. The — appeareth, and the tender grass. *Prov. 27:25*
4. Smite with thine hand, and — with thy foot. *Ezek. 6:11*
9. Ye take — much upon you. *Num. 16:3*
12. I was left —ne, and saw this great vision. *Dan. 10:8*
13. — (American spelling) thy father and mother. *Eph. 6:2*
14. Ought not this woman . . . be loosed from this b—? *Luke 13:16*
15. Who shall — him up? *Gen. 49:9*
17. Water — upon them out of heaven. *II Sam. 21:10*
19. This — shall have put on immortality. *I Cor. 15:54*
21. Adam and —
22. Save me, and I shall be —. *Jer. 17:14*
24. On the seventh day God — his work. *Gen. 2:2*
28. Let there — light. *Gen. 1:3*
30. Ye observe days, and months, . . . and —. *Gal. 4:10*
32. He came thither unto a —, and lodged there. *I Ki. 19:9*
33. How long will it be — they believe me? *Num. 14:11*
35. I have gathered my myrrh with my —. *Song 5:1*
37. Our word toward you was not — and nay. *II Cor. 1:18*
38. I . . . will — forth my sword out of his sheath. *Ezek. 21:3*
40. One — happeneth to them all. *Eccles. 2:14*
42. Seek, and ye shall fi—. *Matt. 7:7*
43. Abraham buried — his wife. *Gen. 23:19*
45. — into his gates with thanksgiving. *Ps. 100:4*
47. They shall be your —uge from the avenger. *Josh. 20:3*

49. The second row shall be an emerald . . . and a —d. *Ex. 28:18*
52. A bride adorneth — with her jewels. *Isa. 61:10*
56. Like a — or a swallow, so did I chatter. *Isa. 38:14*
57. — no man any thing. *Rom. 13:8*
58. The city was — and great. *Neh. 7:4*
60. He casteth forth his —. . . : who can stand before his cold? *Ps. 147:17*
61. He — them forth by the right way. *Ps. 107:7*
62. The aged arose, and — up. *Job 29:8*
63. The men . . . ai— him in the killing of his brethren. *Judg. 9:24*

DOWN

1. Look well to him, and do him no —. *Jer. 39:12*
2. My friends stand —f . . . my kinsmen stand afar off. *Ps. 38:11*
3. The battle is not —, but God's. *II Chr. 20:15*
4. We were binding —. . . and, lo, my sheaf arose. *Gen. 37:7*
5. I will go — them. *Ezek. 38:11*
6. Samson — Delilah
7. It is — blessed to give than to receive. *Acts 20:35*
8. Neither can they — the things whereof they now accuse me. *Acts 24:13*
9. Let them shout from the — of the mountains. *Isa. 42:11*
10. Two are better than —. *Eccles. 4:9*
11. The — number of them is to be redeemed. *Num. 3:48*
16. He should not — long in the place. *Hos. 13:13*

18. The one owed five hundred —e. *Luke 7:41*
20. By my God have I —d over a wall. *II Sam. 22:30*
23. As smoke is driven away, so — them away. *Ps. 68:2*
25. Shew forth his salvation from day to —. *Ps. 96:2*
26. Let me be weighed in an — balance. *Job 31:6*
27. He is risen from the —. *Matt. 14:2*
28. They shall rest in their —. *Isa. 57:2*
29. I have a secret —nd unto thee, O king. *Judg. 3:19*
31. I will a— into heaven. *Isa. 14:13*
34. Give ye —, and hear. *Isa. 28:23*
36. Every man is tempted . . . and —. *James 1:14*
39. From whence come — and fightings among you? *James 4:1*
41. Consider this, . . . lest I — you in pieces. *Ps. 50:22*
44. Thou settest a print upon the — of my feet. *Job 13:27*
46. When she saw the ark . . . she sent he— (2 words) to fetch it. *Ex. 2:5*
48. He bowed down . . . and fell — on his face. *Num. 22:31*
50. God speaketh —, yea twice. *Job 33:14*
51. They that be whole — not a physician. *Matt. 9:12*
52. Take not thy —y spirit from me. *Ps. 51:11*
53. He shall take two he lambs . . . and one — lamb. *Lev. 14:10*
54. He made a covering . . . of rams' skins dyed —. *Ex. 36:19*
55. They walked to and —. *Zech. 6:7*
59. Let us — into the house. *Ps. 122:1*

64

Medium

ACROSS

1. Marathon, for one
5. Bobbins
11. Was the sire of, old style
12. Bed cover
13. "Aida," for one
14. Actor's part
15. Depart
16. Tear; rip
17. Space
18. Kind of evergreen
19. Conclusion
20. Chicago area (with "the")
21. Out of
22. Wrigley Field, for one
24. Showy flower
25. Picnic pest
26. Ocean
27. Mode
30. Vacation home
34. Elm or maple
35. Word with "glass" or "hard"
36. Game show host Barker
37. Wharf rodent
38. Carried out
39. Snatch
40. Check-casher's need: abbr.
41. Spanish painter
42. Fry quickly and lightly
43. Conveyance
45. "— down," became quiet
46. Worn away
47. Poker stake

DOWN

1. Mend one's ways
2. List of things to be done
3. Comical person
4. Greek letter
5. Sailing vessel
6. Tropical tree
7. Small bill
8. Approve
9. Word with "Foreign" or "American"
10. Raging; turbulent
11. Drills
12. Sweeper's need
17. Defeat overwhelmingly
18. To-and-—, back and forth
20. Short letter
21. Daring deed
23. Valley
24. Ballplayer Rose
26. Tender
27. Struggle
28. Merchant
29. Thus far
30. White-water craft
31. Sudden; unexpected
32. Style of beard
33. Receded
35. Earth
38. Gambling cubes
39. Profit
41. Among: poetic
42. Mineral spring
44. Entertainer, Don —

ACROSS

1. Mah-jongg piece
5. Recipe abbreviation
9. Compass point
12. Citrus drinks
13. A color
14. Weeding tool
15. Actor Dillon
16. Plant stem part
17. Endless time period
18. Turf
20. Nourishing substance
22. Associate
25. First State: abbr.
26. — *pro nobis*
27. Unrestrained
29. Sunset direction
32. Type
33. Word with "wave" or "basin"
35. Highway: abbr.
36. Service charges
38. Antitoxins
39. Retreat
40. Triumphant exclamation
42. "The Sound of Music" star
44. Torment
47. Black or Red
48. Sandwich bread
49. Rainbow goddess
51. Thick mass
54. A Gershwin
55. All: prefix
56. Of aircraft: prefix
57. Actor Gibson
58. Scolds continually
59. Ship's forward part

DOWN

1. Highland headgear
2. Gilbert and Sullivan princess
3. Popular TV game show: 4 wds.
4. Bar legally
5. Spigot
6. Open and aboveboard: hyph. wd.
7. Influence
8. Savory
9. High-powered entrepreneur: hyph. wd.
10. Shortly
11. Left
19. Adroit
21. Feline sound
22. Style, as hair
23. Heraldic band
24. Goddess of discord
28. Merit
30. Ragout
31. "Sawbucks"
34. Fellows
37. That woman
41. Plane: French
43. Summarize
44. Hat part
45. "Jane —," Brontë novel
46. "— La Douce"
50. Sibling's nickname
52. Gold: Spanish
53. Rope fiber

Hard

66

Medium

ACROSS

1. Mom's mate
4. Drove too fast
8. Heathen
13. Young woman
17. Hearing organ
18. Become weary
19. Speak eloquently
20. Leaves out
22. Benefited
24. A triangle has three of these
25. Soap opera, for one
27. Deface
28. Utilized
30. At that time
32. Falsehood
33. Conspiracy
35. Confronted
37. Arctic
39. Penny
40. Not at home
41. Sticky stuff
42. Peace symbols
43. Expenses
44. Raw metal
45. Huge boats
46. Was fond of

47. Morose
48. Lessens
50. Be indecisive
51. Revokes
55. Bright color
56. Metric volume
57. Change residences
58. Edgar Allan —, author
59. Boasts
62. Writing material
63. More intelligent
64. Fish eggs
65. Unusual
66. Provide food, as for a party
67. More offensive
68. Speech impediment
69. Thoroughfare: abbr.
70. Goliath's foe
71. Employs
72. Burrowing animals
73. Nine's follower
74. Prophetic sign
75. Ice-cream holders
76. Cushion
77. Sloped
79. Adjusted, as a guitar
80. Mom and Dad
84. Moray, for one
85. Challenges
86. Aching
87. Lubricate
88. Gets larger
91. Uses a stopwatch
92. Closes
93. Pekoe, for one
94. Yours and mine
95. Adored
96. Photographs
97. Trade center
98. Terminate
99. Identical
100. Wharf
101. Baby apron
102. Uses a pressure cooker
104. Beauty shop
107. Foot levers
112. Wooden shoe
113. Inanimate object
114. Sunrise direction
115. Mooselike animal
116. Piano supports

117. Satisfies fully
118. Tints
119. Like a fox

DOWN

1. Energy
2. Boat paddle
3. Advanced
4. Mix
5. Cherry center
6. Before: poetic
7. Subtracts
8. Asked (a question)
9. Very dry
10. Wander about idly
11. Consumed
12. Snuggled
13. Vanquished one
14. So be it!
15. Knight's title
16. Fence steps
21. Very holy person
23. Obese
26. Allows
29. Observe
31. Possesses
33. Needy
34. Entice
35. Got along
36. Inquires
37. Card game
38. Above
39. ZIP —
41. Steps
42. Underwater worker
43. Prank
46. After now
47. Cut off
49. Egg (on)
50. Rubbed (with a cloth)
51. Thorny flowers
52. Rainy month
53. On the —, free
54. Oozes
56. Ancient language
57. Actress, Vera —
59. Unruly children
60. Fray
61. Hockey site
62. Surfaced (a road)
63. Telegraphed
66. Desert animal

67. Climbing plants
68. Vein of metal ore
70. — on, is foolishly fond of
71. Sharpens
72. Equine females
75. Made well
76. Actor's roles
78. What reporters seek
79. Docile
80. Sulk

81. Dignitaries
82. Row, as of opera seats
83. Bed board
85. Strips; takes away
86. Gypped
88. Leaves
89. Undersized animals
90. Severe trial
91. Male turkey
92. That woman
95. Endures

96. Croons
97. Center: prefix
99. Fog and smoke
100. Corn bread
101. Baseball sticks
103. Lincoln, to friends
105. So that's it!
106. Ignited
108. Bolger or Milland
109. Compass point
110. Building extension
111. "Pie in the —"

67

Easy

ACROSS

1. Golf peg
4. Postage sticker
9. That girl
12. Miss Gardner
13. Thick soup
14. Statute
15. Act
17. Rope loop
19. Footed vase
20. Break suddenly
21. Publish, as a newspaper
24. Restaurant employees
27. Let out (money) at interest
28. Donates
29. Wow!
30. Also
31. Loses color
32. Rod used in billiards
33. Compass point
34. Valleys
35. Very large
36. Knitted garment
38. Writer's need
39. Dull routines
40. Distant
41. Sun-dried brick
43. Rugs
47. Father
48. Chimney emission
50. By way of
51. Single unit
52. Records (music)
53. Picnic pest

DOWN

1. Strike lightly
2. Eden resident
3. Hearing organ
4. Baseball, for one
5. Rotate
6. Sofa part
7. Augusta's State: abbr.
8. Certain coins
9. Incline; slant
10. Owns
11. Ram's mate
16. Nest egg, for example
18. Cereal grains
20. Is economical
21. Schemes
22. Extend, as a lease
23. Hoosier State: abbr.
24. Broader
25. Red: French
26. Transparent
28. Strong winds
31. Most plump
32. Saucer's partner
34. Smear on (plaster)
35. "Heavenly" instrument
37. Wear away
38. Peels
40. Not real
41. Excitement
42. Mr. Rather
43. Policeman
44. A Gabor
45. Soft metal
46. Took a chair
49. Pa's mate

ACROSS

1. Certain golf club
7. Forest clearings
13. Baltimore team player
14. Rat, for one
15. *C'est — vie*, that's life!
16. "Fake" medicine
18. Leave
19. Writing fluid
21. Glasgow natives
22. Fish part
23. Weekday: abbr.
25. Huge cask
26. A horse has one
27. Tries
29. Treats badly
31. Foot digit
32. Fire residue
33. Of Spring
36. Arab VIPs
39. Nautical term
40. Scottish interjection
42. Finished
43. "— Abner"
44. Actor Jourdan
46. Mr. Hentoff
47. Exists
48. Olive stuffer
50. New England State: abbr.
51. Bind into a bundle
53. Animal's burrow
55. Shot two under par
56. Not sharp; blunt

DOWN

1. Civil
2. Distant planet
3. Scale note
4. Spinning toy
5. Building additions
6. Responds
7. — Green, Scottish border village
8. Certain tennis strokes
9. Fuss
10. From: French
11. Locomotive
12. Small rocks
17. Neck: French
20. Small falcon
22. Current style
24. European river
26. Pondered
28. Affirmative vote
30. Scrooge's word
33. Hand luggage
34. Hebrew prophet
35. Appeared, threateningly
36. An Oriental religion
37. Rogues
38. Colonize
41. Billiards stick
44. Dwell
45. Part of a ticket
48. Chum
49. Canadian province: abbr.
52. For example: abbr.
54. Greek letter

68

Hard

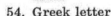

69

Easy

ACROSS

1. Tear
4. Belt location
9. Strange
12. Highest playing card
13. Knight's suit
14. Female deer
15. Five pairs
16. Short swim
17. Overhead
19. Urgent request
21. Crossed the goal line
22. Tartan, for one
24. Face parts
25. Actor's part
26. Complain childishly
27. Behold!
29. There are 12 in a foot: abbr.
30. Object
31. Family room
32. Myself
33. Pine Tree State
34. Authentic
35. Christmas visitor
36. Very short time
37. Alter
39. Arrive
40. Tourist's stopover
41. Against
42. Old horse
45. Florida's country: abbr.
46. Evade
48. Health resort
49. Males
50. Social appointments
51. "Electric" fish

DOWN

1. Large, mouse-like creature
2. Frost (a cake)
3. Correspondents: 2 wds.
4. Walked in water
5. Operatic solo
6. Mischievous child
7. Therefore
8. Following
9. Scents
10. Bird of peace
11. Ownership paper
18. Skeleton part
20. Falsehood
21. Gleam
22. Stuffy; proper
23. Solitary
24. Peking's country
26. Color of snow
27. Plant part
28. Sole
30. Snarled
31. Protection (against)
33. Lion's tresses
34. Border
35. The Devil
36. John Paul —, Revolutionary naval officer
37. Pal
38. Stockings
39. Secret writing
41. Use scissors
43. Mimic
44. Girl
47. Musical tone

ACROSS

1. River bottom
4. Partiality
8. A pair
11. Declare openly
13. Des Moines' State
14. Possessed
15. Cereal grain
16. Arrow's target: hyph. wd.
18. — out, say without thinking
20. Plant juice
21. Chaplin's hat
24. Netherlands natives
28. That woman
30. Eye part
32. Food store, for short
33. Historic period
34. Word with "boy" or "clip"
36. Boy
37. Peru's capital
39. Remove, in printing
40. Female sheep
41. Oyster gem
43. Thick slices
45. Small child
47. Agreements
50. Truman's State
55. London district
56. Expert
57. Bowline or clove hitch
58. Twirled
59. Oolong, for one
60. Satisfy fully
61. Omelet ingredient

DOWN

1. Biting remark
2. Wicked
3. One kind of historical movie
4. Apron top
5. Debt note
6. Piercing tools
7. Lettuce dish
8. Definite article
9. Method
10. Lyric poem
12. Existed
17. Potato
19. Journey
22. Thin nail
23. Oh, no!
25. Astronomer's need
26. Talon
27. Conceal
28. Aid
29. Great Lake
31. Vend
35. Harvest
38. Dance and drama
42. Appearance
44. Male voice
46. Albacore
48. Hoodlum
49. Ballad
50. Gym pad
51. Frozen water
52. Ocean
53. Decay
54. Native: suffix

Medium

71

Hard

ACROSS

1. Cut with scissors
5. Fragment; shed
10. Artist's stand
15. Dressed
19. Final passage: music
20. Make joyful
21. Weeping figure in Greek mythology
22. Healthy; sound
23. Run —, rush around in a frenzy
24. Participant in a speed contest
25. Orb
26. Verdi opera
27. Childbirth is one kind
29. Man's nickname
31. Transportation line's end
33. Rational
34. The Earth
36. Doe, for one
37. Sheen: Brit. sp.
40. Pine, spruce or fir
42. Fine table linen
46. Kind of tooth filling
47. Remote
48. Former Argentine leader
50. Florida city
51. Yemen's capital
52. Hesitate
54. Finger or toe
56. Close by
57. Regret
58. Hiker's ailment
60. Annoyed
62. Summer: French
63. Part; sunder
65. Sweetheart
67. Actor McGavin
69. Party: slang
70. Marry again
71. Nip; use teeth
72. Even though
75. Challenged
76. Salad garnishes
80. Nautical chain
81. Edited out
83. Lightest known metal
85. Young child
86. Drunkards
88. Ancient souvenir
90. — and whey
91. Lab heating apparatus
92. Go in
94. Massenet opera
96. Falsehood
97. Vote in
98. Refuge
100. Stirs up; rouses
102. Evening party
103. Small bottle
105. Stories
106. Vocalize
107. Year's "schedule"
111. 2,000 lbs.
112. Having good judgment
116. Retired for the evening
117. Love: French
119. With one
121. Forehead
122. Plod (through)
123. New Zealand native
124. Ancient Scandinavian
125. Bowling alley
126. Actress Daly
127. English county
128. Certain woolen cloth
129. Sight organs

DOWN

1. A food fish
2. Alaskan city
3. False god
4. India's neighbor
5. Calm
6. Irish county
7. Risqué
8. Consumed
9. Human being
10. Overwhelmed
11. Be ill
12. Fireplace soil
13. Receded
14. Looked at slyly
15. Committee head
16. Reclined
17. Actor Robert or Alan
18. Distribute cards
28. Diversify
30. Journey
32. Steak, for one
34. Least good
35. Came from a source
37. Fibbers
38. Excessive
39. Slumber
40. Bring about
41. Actor Moore
43. Moslem prince
44. Flash flood
45. Actress Valentine
47. Utter confidence
49. Refusal: slang
52. Wall coating
53. Kind of fisherman
55. Boring; wearisome
58. Plait
59. Wheel on a spur
61. Fact
64. Lincoln, for short
66. Early form of Sanskrit
68. Prepare flax
70. Shining brightly
71. Groom's partner
72. Bewildered: 2 wds.
73. City on the Rhone
74. Mrs. Gerald Ford, familiarly

75. City in India
76. Tennis' Mrs. Lloyd
77. Playful mammal
78. Time being
79. Iowa, for one
82. Allow
84. Large bulrushes
87. Fabric edge
89. Scar
91. Legally qualified

93. Spoil
95. Farm structure
97. Huge time periods
99. Mrs.: French
101. Renting inhabitant
102. Burned slightly
104. Lorenzo — of TV's "Falcon Crest"
106. Perceive
107. Throw; fling

108. Skillfully
109. Mr. Spinks
110. Certain Australian beasts, for short
112. Painful
113. Donkey's sound
114. Solitary
115. Female sheep
118. Yorkshire river
120. Not high

72

ACROSS

1. Leap, as a frog
4. Did the crawl
8. Male deer
12. Actress Gardner
13. Detest
14. Story
15. Knock
16. Exist
17. Dining room feature
18. Abundance
20. Weep; cry
21. Dull routine
22. School certificate
26. Exclamation of surprise
28. At no time
30. First garden
31. Crimson
33. Black bird
35. Newsman Rather
36. Baby's bed
38. Steamship
40. Musical tone
41. With expectation
43. Chewing treat
45. Golf item
46. Drowsy
49. Dish
52. Take to court
53. Also
54. Assistant
55. Heroic poem
56. Inquire
57. Film, "The — Hunter"
58. Dillon of "Gunsmoke"
59. Actor Marvin

DOWN

1. "Celestial" instrument
2. Elliptical
3. Daily publication
4. Break into many pieces
5. Cautious
6. Dined
7. Myself
8. Horse "house"
9. Bill; check
10. Everything
11. Golly!
17. Summit
19. Holy sister
20. Warning sound
22. Satan
23. Peculiar
24. Dinner is one
25. Dancer Pavlova
26. Curved form
27. Brave man
29. Worth
32. Dunk
34. Ignore
37. More desirable
39. Regret
42. Service charge
44. Steel is one
46. Befit
47. Sit for an artist
48. Harness (for oxen)
49. Cushion; mat
50. Falsehood
51. Fruit drink
52. Health resort
55. Type measure

Easy

73

ACROSS

1. Belfry flyer
4. Take an oath
9. Graceful tree
12. Actress Gabor
13. Rental document
14. Miss Remick
15. More ahead of time
17. Heavenly body
19. Writing fluid
20. Wavers (between)
21. "It's — way to Tipperary": 2 wds.
24. Congo or Nile
25. Bail out (water)
26. Phony person
27. Father
29. Also
30. Breadmaker
31. Light-brown
32. Compass point
33. Attempts
34. Tie together
35. Simmers
36. Ready cash
37. Bed linens
39. Cut the grass
40. Breakfast staple
41. "A — stone . . ."
45. Miller or Blyth
46. Girl in "Little House on the Prairie"
48. Payable
49. Of course!
50. Glowing coal
51. Picnic pest

DOWN

1. "Busy" insect
2. Miss Gardner
3. Asphalting
4. Support for a broken arm
5. Saturday to Saturday
6. Corn spike
7. While
8. Regain (health)
9. Gantry of fiction
10. Malicious look
11. N.Y.C. baseball team
16. Face wrinkle
18. Above
20. Long walks
21. Expression of dismay
22. Country road
23. Strange
24. Tidies the yard
26. Flunks
27. Window glass
28. Actor Griffith
30. Peanut —, candy choice
31. Sardine can
33. Foot parts
34. Soup dish
35. Baked —, Boston dish
36. Grinding tooth
37. Remain
38. Whetstone
39. Greater amount
41. Massage
42. "Apple cider" girl of song
43. Convent dweller
44. Receive
47. "I — Woman"

ACROSS

1. Fundamental
6. Backless chair
11. Extravagant
12. Trimmed (a hedge)
14. Single thing
15. Imbecile
17. Southern State: abbr.
18. Bounder
19. Aroma
20. Scarlet
21. At home
22. Garden tools
23. "On Golden —," film
24. Marred
26. Pal
27. Prayer ending
28. Valley
29. Slides
31. Chaps
34. Heavy weights
35. Circuit breakers
36. Sound of laughter
37. Fish eggs
38. Muggy
39. Humorist
40. Like
41. Recluse
42. Actor Andrews
43. Dot
45. Soccer team number
47. Requires
48. Planted (seeds)

DOWN

1. Tropical fruit
2. Eager
3. Have a chair!
4. Exists
5. Rhode Island Red, for one
6. Twirls
7. Jog
8. Umpire's call
9. Atop
10. Traditional tale
11. Clear; readily understood
13. Papa
16. Feat
19. Wise people
20. Western show
22. Freeway exits
23. Tows
25. Pine Tree State
26. Bundled
28. Craves
29. Thong
30. Make less tight
31. Offensive vapor
32. Whimpered
33. Devil
35. Money available for use
38. Thug: slang
39. Surfing need
41. Recline
42. Moisture on the lawn
44. Scale tone
46. Behold!

MEDIUM

75

HARD

ACROSS

1. Highest point
5. Maui garland
8. Coarse hominy
12. Lend
13. Doctrine suffix
14. Lilylike plant
15. Precious metal
16. Health resort
17. Climbing plant
18. Confidence
20. Lute's kin
22. Pay court to
23. Self
24. Winter, for one
27. Bushy plants
31. Everything
32. Service charge
33. Abundance
37. Colombia city
40. Be in debt
41. Ventilate
42. Boy Scout group
45. Casual trousers
49. Declare openly
50. — Vegas, Nevada
52. Musical sound
53. Arizona river
54. Lyric poem
55. Paradise
56. Small whirlpool
57. Moist
58. Marsh grass

DOWN

1. A seaweed
2. Hen's house
3. Shopping complex
4. Gives funds for
5. Capital of Portugal
6. Sixth sense
7. Likenesses
8. Rescuer
9. Dismounted
10. Da Vinci's "— Lisa"
11. Equal
19. Cow sound
21. Cry of disgust
24. Plant juice
25. Building wing
26. Pub brew
28. Flying saucer, for one
29. Wager
30. Ocean
34. Oslo's country
35. One plus one
36. Lemony color
37. Woeful-looking dog breed
38. Lubricant
39. Kitchen tool
42. Book leaf
43. Eager
44. Narrated
46. Signal system
47. Leg joint
48. Dispatch
51. Fruit drink

ACROSS

1. Task; chore
4. Competent
8. Graceful bird
12. Reverent wonder
13. Tidy
14. Ice-cream holder
15. Went back on a promise
17. Big
18. Always
19. Signaled with an eye
20. Direct attention (to something)
22. That woman
23. Crafty
24. Ireland, poetically
25. Asian country
27. Appointment
28. Fedora or sombrero
29. Petty quarrel
33. Arrange in folds
35. Heroic legend
36. Vim
39. Exist
40. Pretend: 2 wds.
41. — from, not subject to (as taxes)
43. Sharp-tasting
44. Swagger
45. Competition
48. Baseball great Speaker
49. Sound a horn
50. Sprint
51. Auction
52. Irritable
53. Tennis-court feature

DOWN

1. Jolt or shock
2. Be in debt (to)
3. Receive an advantage (from)
4. Wrath
5. Foamy brew
6. Boy
7. Lovable alien: abbr.
8. Glance at quickly
9. Has a job
10. Michael Landon TV role
11. Poor
16. Equalized in number
17. Mortgage
19. Word with "bread" or "cap"
20. Scarlet
21. Notable age
22. Body contour
25. Map
26. State positively
30. Dressmaker's guide
31. In the past
32. Tawny
34. Completely engrossed
36. Annoying people
37. Additional
38. Danger
40. Tall and lean
42. Ponder (over)
43. Chinese association
45. Food fish
46. Take to court
47. Powerful explosive: abbr.
49. That man

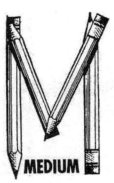

MEDIUM

77

HARD

ACROSS

1. Fruity spread
4. Electric cord
8. Prophet
12. "We — the World"
13. Culture medium
14. — boy!: 2 wds.
15. Native American: abbr.
16. Garment for Tarzan
18. Dawdles
20. Sharpens
21. Clump of ivy
22. Cupid
24. Memorable ages
26. Russian monarch: var. sp.
27. Guy's date
30. Uproar
32. Put a new surface on
34. Dined
35. — out, allot
37. Comic Johnson
38. Examine closely
39. Energy unit
40. Clip wool from
43. Ameliorate
47. TV sitcom: 2 wds.
49. Senate vote, perhaps
50. Length x width
51. Earth: prefix
52. French article
53. Dogwalker's command
54. Off the —, incorrect
55. Before: poetic

DOWN

1. Incarcerate
2. Pisa's river
3. Practice a form of yoga
4. Like corduroy
5. Stravinsky
6. Union achievements
7. Sea eagle
8. Rural sights
9. English prep school
10. Ducal family
11. Game cheers
17. Hard task
19. Nonsense!: British
23. Uncommon
24. Government bureau: abbr.
25. Twaddle: slang
26. Crystal formation
27. Grotesque ornament
28. Function (as)
29. Grant, for one
31. Grinding mineral
33. M*A*S*H star
36. Priority system
38. Pertaining to John Paul II
39. English Derby town
40. Former ruler
41. Jack rabbit
42. Fencing sword
44. Woman's name
45. Swerve
46. Alleviate
48. Small flatfish

78

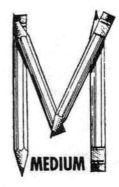

MEDIUM

ACROSS

1. Untidy person
5. Recedes, as the tide
9. Spouse
13. Forehead
17. Do road resurfacing
18. Plane maneuver
19. Sharp; tart
20. Pencil mark
21. Small bill
22. Lawbreaking pedestrian
24. From that time
25. Goals
27. Tall, slender grass
28. Deposited money, for example
29. Actress Grant
30. Tie
31. Submerged
32. Antic
35. Provide money for
36. Distributes: 2 wds.
40. Mr. Alda
41. Crooned
42. Tries out
43. Des Moines' country: abbr.
44. Males
45. Be in need of
46. Estimate
47. Pace
48. Easter activity: 2 wds.
50. Breezy
51. Sheriff's band
52. Expert
53. Pigeon's relatives
54. Evil
55. Large piece
58. Arness or Brolin
59. Car shelters
63. Standing; position
64. Baker's —, thirteen
65. Fine fur
66. Ms. Arden
67. Actress MacGraw
68. "The Road Not —," Frost poem
69. Hospital division
70. Principal
71. Improved
73. Donahue or Silvers
74. Universe
75. Copies
76. Bucket
77. Brooks or Torme
78. Spoiled; damaged
81. Belfry residents
82. Resist: 2 wds.
86. Astound
87. From the original source
89. By way of
90. Miss Minnelli
91. Make cookies
92. Highway division
93. Gasp
94. Paradise
95. Lyric poems
96. Nervous
97. Pub drinks

DOWN

1. Stain
2. Ms. Turner
3. Ended
4. Exist
5. Overjoy
6. Young men
7. Curtsy
8. Careful; frugal
9. Roused from sleep
10. Frosted, as a cake
11. Evergreen
12. Actor Asner
13. Flashes on and off
14. Skating area
15. "— upon a time . . ."
16. Unwanted plant
22. Scoff (at)
23. Give temporarily
24. Smooths (wood)
26. Singer Campbell
28. Certain infield hits
30. Ship's bed
31. Impudent
32. Arrived
33. "Shake —," hurry: 2 wds.
34. Twinge
35. Statistic
36. Listens to
37. Ins and —, all the details
38. Consumes
39. Record (music)
41. Not crazy
42. Melodies
45. Good fortune
46. Donated
47. Soft drink
49. Country singer Williams
50. Females
51. Position (a car)
53. Stunned
54. Musical group
55. Peevish person
56. American patriot, Nathan —
57. Single item
58. Stories with punch lines
59. Lass
60. Equipment

61. Wicked
62. Transmit
64. Challenged
65. Letters, packages, etc.
68. Indian house
69. Train signal
70. Shape

72. Cheetah's master
73. Butter squares
74. Fuse heated metal
76. Peels
77. Dollars, for example
78. Masculine
79. Among
80. Tear down; demolish

81. Two-wheeler
82. Dangle
83. Egg-shaped
84. Legal penalty
85. Lards
87. Passing style
88. Owned
91. Actress Derek
93. Father

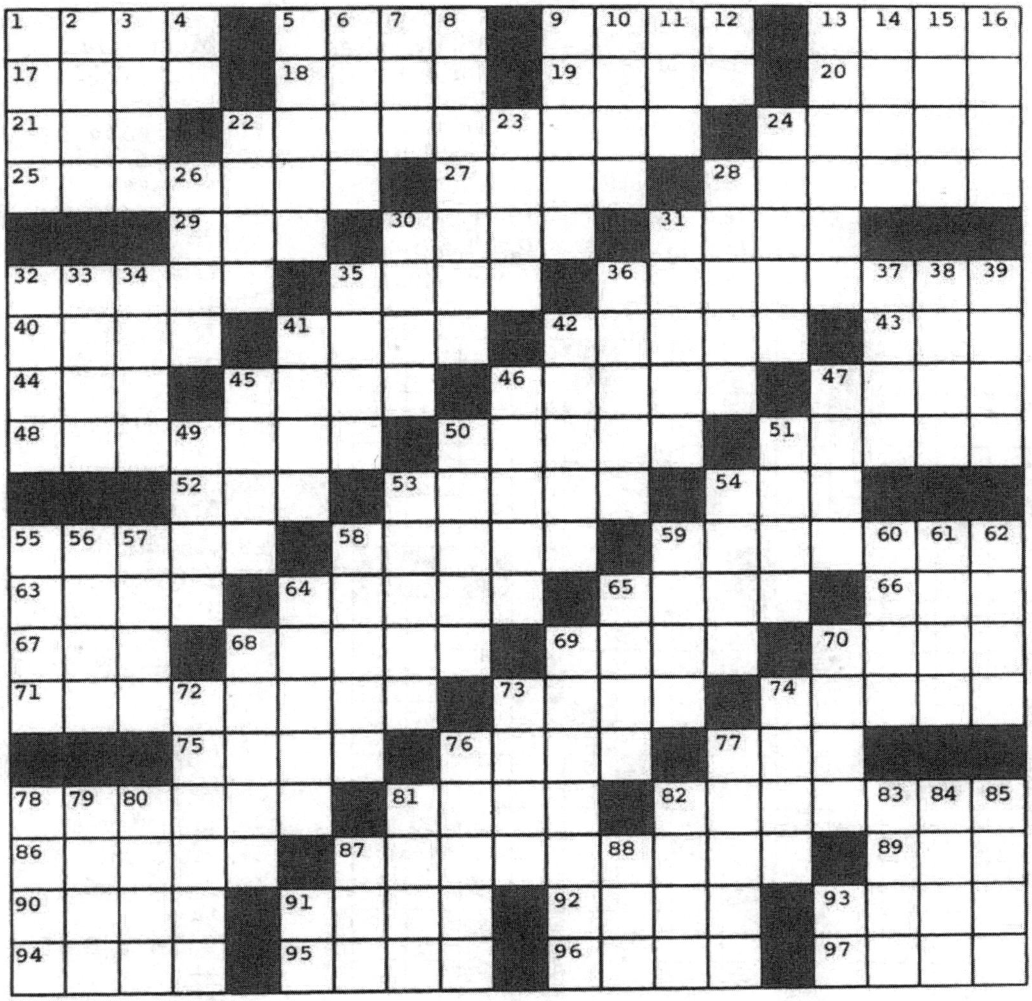

79

MEDIUM

ACROSS

1. Self-esteem
4. Soft drink
8. "King of the jungle"
12. Faucet
13. Burden
14. Advantage, as in sports
15. Made a formal request (for)
17. Sleep noisily
18. Lubricates
19. Sounded taps
20. Fragrant blooms
22. Haven, for ships
23. Enthusiastic
24. Next-door friend
28. Ran into
29. Theater passage
30. Fish eggs
31. Foretells
33. Labyrinth
34. Lyric poems
35. Wove (a chair seat)
36. Alcoholic drink: slang
39. Slipped
40. Leases
41. Extended across
44. Choir member
45. Vichyssoise, for one
46. Stat for Dwight Gooden: abbr.
47. Color changer
48. Taverns
49. Grimly humorous

DOWN

1. Greek vowel
2. Mountain pass
3. Facing
4. Stains
5. Dollar bills
6. Failure, as a firecracker
7. Like
8. Distance from end to end
9. Object of devotion
10. Monster
11. Must have
16. Told falsehoods
17. Sudden increase, as in voltage
19. Cooks pasta
20. Highway access road
21. In excess of
22. Nuisances
24. More agreeable
25. Unused: hyph. wd.
26. Seep
27. Marsh grass
29. Assistants
32. Physician
33. Principal pipe line
35. Applauds
36. Thin nail
37. Depend (upon)
38. — up, pay
39. Made thread
41. Male child
42. Make a mistake
43. Actress, Doris —
45. Yes: Spanish

ACROSS

1. Weasel's "sound"
4. Skin on the top and back of the head
9. That girl
12. Hearing organ
13. Complete
14. Shy; bashful
15. Supply
17. Wed secretly
19. Mickey and Minnie
20. Shadowed: slang
21. Use one's brain
23. Sat for a painting
24. Stockings
25. Corn cakes
26. Exist
28. Pub drink
29. Turns ashen
30. Tin container
31. You and I
32. Sleeveless cloaks
33. Musical group
34. Merchandise
35. Grades; ratings
36. Chauffeur
38. Walking stick
39. Grow mellow
40. Forest wardens
43. High card
44. "Believe me, if all — endearing young charms . . ."
46. Rodent
47. Marry
48. Factions
49. Secret agent

DOWN

1. Brisk energy
2. Canoe paddle
3. Vow
4. Adhere
5. Morse, for one
6. Had lunch
7. Creole State: abbr.
8. Satisfies
9. Upbraid
10. Expect wishfully
11. Watched closely
16. Climbing plant
18. Falsehoods
20. Musical sounds
21. Melt
22. Gopher's home
23. Vaulting aids
25. Writing need
26. Financial institution
27. Concludes
29. Mothers and fathers
30. Professions
32. Cavern
33. Loud noise
34. Dried, as dishes
35. Lions' long hair
36. Sketch
37. Paddy crop
38. Lawsuit
40. Fishing pole
41. Knock sharply
42. Pigpen
45. Informal greeting

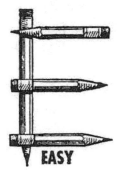

EASY

81 BIBLE CROSSWORD   MEDIUM

by RUSS CARLEY

Bible references in this puzzle are from the King James Version. You'll find it stimulating to solve, and may discover you know more Bible than you think you do.

ACROSS

1. Slayer of Goliath
6. King Solomon gave unto the queen of — all her desire. *I Ki. 10:13*
11. — not evil against thy neighbour. *Prov. 3:29*
12. They have taken — from Lebanon to make masts. *Ezek. 27:5*
14. Be ye . . . perfect — as your Father. *Matt. 5:48*
15. Man shall not live by —ad alone. *Matt. 4:4*
17. He which converteth the sinner from the —r of his way shall save a soul from death. *James 5:20*
18. Love of —y is the root of all evil. *I Tim. 6:10*
19. Let them shout from the — of the mountains. *Isa. 42:11*
20. Though your sins be as scarlet, they shall be as white as —. *Isa. 1:18*
21. The kingdom of heaven is — hand. *Matt. 3:2*
22. In four quarters were the porters, toward the east, west, north, and —. *I Chr. 9:24*
24. — dwell in him, and he in us. *I John 4:13*
25. There is a kinsman — than I. *Ruth 3:12*
28. — the devil, and he will flee from you. *James 4:7*
31. The first — shall be a sardius, a topaz, and a carbuncle. *Ex. 28:17*
32. I — no pleasant bread. *Dan. 10:3*
33. The glory of this — house shall be greater than of the former. *Hag. 2:9*
36. The Jews should be ready . . . to — themselves on their enemies. *Esth. 8:13*
39. Peace — earth. *Luke 12:51*
40. Give us this day our — bread. *Matt. 6:11*
42. The Lord shall be unto thee — everlasting light. *Isa. 60:19*
43. With us are . . . very — men, much elder than thy father. *Job 15:10*
46. For they — not the land . . . by their own sword. *Ps. 44:3*
47. Two of every — shalt thou bring into the ark. *Gen. 6:19*
49. He spread a cloud for a co—ng. *Ps. 105:39*
50. I have been a stranger — (2 wds.) strange land. *Ex. 2:22*
51. Pharaoh's heart was h—ned, neither did he hearken unto them. *Ex. 7:22*
52. Then the — disciples went away into Galilee. *Matt. 28:16*
54. — to Caesar the things that are Caesar's. *Mark 12:17*
56. Oh death, where is thy —? *I Cor. 15:55*
57. My God, why hast thou for—me? *Mark 15:34*

DOWN

1. A man shall — unto the LORD of all that he hath. *Lev. 27:28*
2. In the beginning God created the he— and the earth. *Gen. 1:1*
3. There shall be no grapes on the —. *Jer. 8:13*
4. Blessed — he that cometh in the name of the Lord. *Luke 13:35*
5. There was a certain creditor which had two —s. *Luke 7:41*
6. She hath no strong rod to be a —e to rule. *Ezek. 19:14*
7. — is Lord of lords. *Rev. 17:14*
8. Thou fe—t them with the bread of tears. *Ps. 80:5*

9. Gather the wheat into my —. *Matt. 13:30*
10. Take bow and —. *II Ki. 13:15*
11. This matter is by the decree of the watchers, and the —d by the word of the holy ones. *Dan. 4:17*
13. He that —h iniquity shall reap vanity. *Prov. 22:8*
16. The —gh ways shall be made smooth. *Luke 3:5*
22. They — fig leaves together. *Gen. 3:7*
23. Thy father made our yoke —. *II Chr. 10:10*
26. Thou — my Son. *Heb. 5:5*
27. He . . . chooseth a tree that will not —. *Isa. 40:20*
29. Thou shalt not —al. *Ex. 20:15*
30. The poor is hated . . . but the rich hath many fr—ds. *Prov. 14:20*
33. He took the seven —s and the fishes, and gave thanks. *Matt. 15:36*

34. Thou madest him a little lower than the —. *Heb. 2:7*
35. He arose, and rebuked the wind and the — of the water. *Luke 8:24*
36. A people that . . . burneth incense upon — of brick. *Isa. 65:3*
37. The LORD God planted a — eastward in Eden. *Gen. 2:8*
38. — into his gates with thanksgiving. *Ps. 100:4*
41. A young l— roared against him. *Judg. 14:5*
44. He rememb—h the obedience of you all. *II Cor. 7:15*
45. God —ded the light from the darkness. *Gen. 1:4*
47. They — as lead in the mighty waters. *Ex. 15:10*
48. Set thine house in —r. *II Ki. 20:1*
53. The T— Commandments
55. —t, drink, and be merry. *Luke 12:19*

82

EASY

ACROSS

1. Track event
5. Stitches (together)
9. Biblical "you"
13. Employer
17. Golf club
18. Applaud
19. Debtor's notes
20. Tidy
21. Pod vegetable
22. Errand person
24. Stage in development
25. Kind of cracker
27. College student
28. Fancy feathers
29. Single
30. Fashion's Christian —
31. Fright
32. Weighing device
35. Lend
36. Sowing
40. Magician's stick
41. Healthy
42. Not taut
43. Can material
44. Fitting; appropriate
45. Bargain
46. Disgrace
47. Singer Horne
48. Affirmative reply
49. Terminate
50. Small rock
51. Halley's, for one
52. Rodent
53. Bride's color
54. Severed
55. Tardier
58. Smiles
59. Taxi
60. Used a chair
63. Tart
64. Carry (to)
65. Drill (a hole)
66. Bakery item
67. Raw metal
68. Chalkboard
69. Uncover
70. Lateral surface
71. What a sweetheart sings under your window
73. Thorny flower
74. Skeleton pieces
75. Title
76. Heal
77. Sticky stuff: slang
78. Flee from
81. Hired man
82. Citrus fruits
86. Condemns
87. Rider
89. Stadium cheer
90. Not busy
91. Challenge
92. Unusual
93. Bee house
94. Lofty
95. Bullfight cheers: Spanish
96. Went too fast
97. Mimicked

DOWN

1. Tears
2. Region
3. Film, "— Miner's Daughter"
4. Printing measure
5. Play section
6. Otherwise
7. Existed
8. Unique
9. Jungle cat
10. Used a garden tool
11. Belonging to us
12. America, for short: abbr.
13. Not damaged
14. Sewing line
15. Relieve
16. Highways: abbr.
22. Belonging to me
23. Lunch time
24. Wood board
26. Recounted
28. Tranquility
30. Raggedy Ann or Andy
31. Fire offshoot
32. Move gracefully to and fro
33. Cloak
34. Colony insects
35. Heavy metal
36. Jet, for one
37. Article
38. Baseball team number
39. Small insect
41. Left
42. Inoculations
45. Letter beginning
46. Sharp pain
47. Parking area
50. Glisten
51. Sugar piece
52. Crimson
53. Use a pen
54. Show concern
55. Vietnam neighbor
56. Land measure
57. Layer
58. School mark
59. Apple center

60. Twirl
61. Assistant
62. Golf pegs
64. Accuse
65. Foundation
68. Easy things: slang
69. Edges
70. In a little while

72. Glossy paint
73. Stocking woes
74. Wild pig
76. Kinds of containers
77. Avarice
78. Revise
79. Soft drink
80. Learning institu-
tion: abbr.

81. Rabbit's kin
82. Fairy tale monster
83. Tight hold
84. Roof overhang
85. Lean-to
87. Buddy
88. Snooze
91. Wedding vow word
93. Laugh sound

83

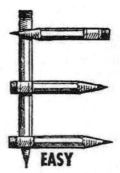

EASY

ACROSS

1. The Mediterranean, for one
4. Dog's foot
7. Heavenly body
8. Monetary penalties
10. Push roughly
11. Make believe
13. Narrow country road
14. Sly look
15. Fawn's mother
16. First woman
17. Belonging to me
18. At this place
19. Go down
21. Disappeared slowly
22. Metallic rock
23. Was victorious
24. Groom's mate
27. Pantries
31. Was carried along (in)
32. Tenderhearted
33. Knock sharply
34. Chimp, for example
35. Chair or bench
36. Walk back and forth
37. Instructor
39. Founded (on)
40. Single-masted sailboat
41. Above
42. Sty resident, perhaps
43. Marry

DOWN

1. Small rocks
2. Roof edge
3. Exist
4. Landing place
5. Picnic pest
6. Did a gardening chore
7. Close —, narrow escape
8. Liberate
9. "Saw wood"
10. Toboggan, for example
11. Await decision
12. Feat of courage
14. Fishing string
17. Nothing more than
18. Word with "bag" or "cuff"
20. ZIP —
21. Gerald —, 38th US President
23. Desire
24. Impudent child
25. Catches with a lasso
26. Perfect models
27. Big fibber
28. Rubbed out
29. Indy-500 car
30. Drove too fast
32. Retain
35. Movie or TV program
36. Surface (a road)
38. Dove's sound
39. Archer's need

ACROSS

1. Mexican dishes
6. French city
11. Natural ability
12. Chicken — soup
14. Pennsylvania city
15. Domed buildings
17. Actress Fabray, for short
18. Metal bolt
19. — and outs
20. Female sheep
21. Mimics
22. Greek letter
23. More flavorful
25. Overparticular
26. Replies
28. Hoaxes
31. Radiators; furnaces
35. Labels
36. Leafy plant
37. Agent: abbr.
38. Hail
39. Abdominal pain
40. Befuddled: Scottish
41. Policeman: French
43. Bird of peace
44. Finale
45. Curdled
47. Health: French
48. Lock of hair

DOWN

1. Pacific island
2. Dress styles: hyph. wd.
3. Alphabet letter
4. Light-switch position
5. Zebra markings
6. Poker stakes
7. Disorderly retreat
8. Actor Chaney
9. Small whirlpools
10. Tilts
11. Doctrine
13. Composition
16. Crush; make helpless
18. Showers
22. Arrest: slang
24. Scottish caps
25. French coin
27. Most spooky
28. Acting platform
29. Sanctuaries
30. Meeting outline
32. Blunders
33. Actor Christopher and family
34. Rapidity
36. Form or shape (metal)
39. Jargon
42. Noise
43. Owing
46. Either's partner

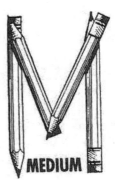

MEDIUM

85

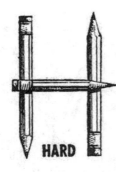

HARD

ACROSS

1. Choir voice
5. Grain holders
9. Fore's opposite
12. Control; check
13. Anglo-Saxon laborer
14. Aegean or Red
15. "She sells sea shells . . . ," e.g.: 2 wds.
18. Not at work
19. Pleases
20. Courtyard
23. Rope fiber
25. Indian agent
26. Husband: French
27. Favoring
30. Insincerely: 3 wds.
33. Storm center
34. Hardy cabbage
35. Of a time period
36. Has charge of
37. Supernumerary
38. Gazelle
41. Feathery scarf
42. Eloquent: hyph. wd.
48. Officeholder: slang
49. Diving bird
50. Off-Broadway theater award
51. Thoroughfares: abbr.
52. Black: poetic
53. Baseball team number

DOWN

1. Craft
2. Mr. Tolstoy
3. Malleable metal
4. Current
5. Gripe: slang
6. Adherent: suffix
7. Compass point
8. Pertaining to earthquake
9. Piedmontese city
10. — of clay
11. Sailors
16. Aerial phenomenon
17. Eat the evening meal
20. Meat paste
21. South China island
22. Prong
23. Greets
24. Sea eagle
26. Bad-tempered
27. Saucy
28. Foster
29. Sooner State: abbr.
31. Arthur Godfrey's instrument
32. Six-cornered figure
36. Pastor: abbr.
37. Endless time period
38. Snakes
39. Read the — act
40. Misfortunes
41. West Germany's capital
43. Carl Reiner's son
44. As well
45. Where: Latin
46. One: German
47. Scottish river

ACROSS

1. Prohibit
4. Liberace's instrument
9. Perform onstage
12. Fruit drink
13. Go inside
14. Female deer
15. Move forward
17. Overhead
19. —, humbug!
20. Traps
21. Motionless
24. National bird
25. Cornmeal cake
26. Unwind
27. Mother
29. Noah's vessel
30. Packing boxes
31. Be victorious
32. Musical tone
33. Jabs; prods
34. Desire
35. Warsaw natives
36. Thick strings
37. Sabers
39. Chum
40. Sample (the food)
41. Breakfast foods
45. Eisenhower's nickname
46. Portion
48. Cow's sound
49. Bright color
50. Carries
51. Use a crowbar

DOWN

1. Sheep's cry
2. Find the sum
3. Gun (a motor)
4. Of punishment
5. Ruler measure
6. Dined
7. Compass point
8. Citrus fruits
9. Idolize
10. Small, sheltered bay
11. Golf ball holders
16. Competent
18. Bouncing toy
20. Rescues
21. Practice boxing
22. Ripped
23. Printer's fluid
24. Relieves
26. Garden tools
27. Obey
28. Picnic pests
30. Most chilly
31. "— Games," 1983 movie
33. Harbor
34. "Big, bad" animal
35. Sat for an artist
36. Coffeehouses
37. Mix
38. Rouse from sleep
39. Unmixed
41. Gym pad
42. Mischievous child
43. Neither's partner
44. — sauce, Chinese food flavoring
47. Santa's word

EASY

87

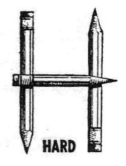

HARD

ACROSS

1. Ornamental green stone
5. Use boastful language
9. Thick slice, as of cheese
13. Sketched
17. Sir Guinness
18. Aviation term
19. Cab
20. Hawkeye State
21. Where wheat is ground
22. Fruit drinks
24. At any time
25. Prepared clams a certain way
27. Like fish, before filleting
28. Provides food for
30. — a girl!
31. Tear apart
32. Sand hill
33. Wild hogs
36. Containing no preservatives
37. Frying pans
41. European mountain range
42. Mix (a salad)
43. Of a blackish or dusky color
44. Keats specialty
45. Insolent talk: slang
46. Merry prank
47. Uses an ax
48. Lobster part
49. Oyster or clam
51. Plant of the mustard family
52. Date trees
53. A long time
54. Exchange
55. Persian elf
56. Syrup-yielding tree
58. Head cooks
59. Frozen desserts
62. Indigo dye
63. Container for salad dressing
64. Othello was one
65. Ration-book agency: abbr.
66. Common suffix
67. Skyrockets
68. College student
69. Not shut
70. Crêpes Suzette and Baked Alaska
72. Menageries
73. Leveled: Brit. sp.
74. Sea eagle
75. Hot cross —
76. Gym pad
77. "I — for ice cream"
80. Brewer's purchase
81. Meals
85. Barren
86. One who loves fine foods
89. Verdi heroine
90. Yawn
91. Pisa's river
92. Auricular
93. Ship's bottom
94. Settled down for the night
95. A Redgrave
96. Lattice slat
97. Anglo-Saxon laborer

DOWN

1. — and jellies
2. Came to rest
3. Proofreader's mark
4. Cream-filled items
5. Large bundles
6. Clarinet part
7. Branch
8. Peanuts
9. Tolerate
10. — -in-waiting
11. Chopping tool
12. Dinner rolls
13. Counted calories
14. Ramble
15. Vase-shaped jug
16. Conflicts
23. Not any
26. Andes, for example: abbr.
29. A Williams
31. Former U.S. Secretary of State
32. Lemon —, candies
33. Fragrant ointment
34. Miscellany
35. Bakery products: 2 wds.
36. One kind of meat
37. Gander's mate
38. Treats for the kids
39. Dutch cheese
40. Bastes
42. Russian news agency
43. Throws off
46. Debussy's "Clair de —"
47. Dexterity
48. Food fish
50. Lounge lazily
51. Canadian Indians
52. Fleshy fruit
54. Part of the week: abbr.
55. Strong stimulus
56. Lass
57. English queen

58. "Jalopy": slang
59. Adversaries
60. Fencing sword
61. Beach material
63. Johnnycake
    ingredient
64. Pasture sounds
67. "Evening" in Venice
68. Hold in check

69. Thin, brittle, baked
    item
71. Like some rye bread
72. African native
73. Sped
75. — and eggs
76. Chew
77. Adventure tale
78. One kind of seafood

79. Perfect for eating,
    as fruit
80. Gopher State: abbr.
81. *Café au —*
82. Hurries
83. Paradise
84. Store event
87. Use a crowbar
88. Greek letter

88

HARD

ACROSS

1. Harbor boat
4. Moist
8. Assorted: abbr.
12. Standards of judgment
14. In the know about: slang
15. Noble
16. Glide along
17. Inexperienced
18. Like a viper's eyes
19. Fireplace tool
22. Severe
24. Other: Latin
25. Kibbutz dance
26. Furniture wood
29. Site of a historical event: 2 wds.
32. Witty remark
33. Old Greek coin
34. Diminutive suffix
35. Belgian town
37. Outdated
38. Very pale
40. Lend a hand
41. Scorch
42. Candid, as a talk: 3 wds.
47. Commands to Dobbin
48. Self-government
49. Actress Sommer
50. Derma
51. Singer Davis

DOWN

1. For shame!
2. Swiss canton
3. Fishing spear
4. Exclude
5. In a line
6. Old Russian village
7. God of flocks
8. Heston role
9. Teamed with and up to no good: 2 wds. (slang)
10. Small earring
11. Frontier scout
13. Menace
18. Boast
19. Tropical tree
20. Mishmash
21. Site of a historic event: 2 wds.
22. Itinerants
23. Seed covering
25. Cupbearer to the gods
27. Painting and dance
28. Body joint
30. Forsaken, of old
31. Directly: hyph. wd.
36. Intrinsically: 2 wds.
37. Climber's aid
38. Tennis great
39. Close tightly
40. Opposition member
42. College degrees: abbr.
43. Arctic bird
44. Dad's mate
45. Doctor's group: abbr.
46. Site of the Flatiron Building: abbr.

ACROSS

1. Be in debt
4. Firm
9. Male turkey
12. In favor of
13. Start the day
14. Self-esteem
15. Dined, Thanksgiving style
17. Approaches
19. Owns
20. Prolonged looks
21. Ambulance alarm
24. Barbecue rod
25. Very dry
26. Health resorts
27. Ask for a handout
30. Boy
31. Valentine symbol
32. Make angry
33. Naval rank: abbr.
34. Poker stake
35. Slender
36. Terminates
37. Cavities
38. Endures
41. Fishing pole
42. Artist's drawing stand
43. Love story
47. Muhammad of boxing
48. Wear away gradually
50. Your and my
51. Afternoon social
52. Drainpipe
53. Kickoff gadget

DOWN

1. Light-switch word
2. — is me!
3. Historical time
4. The Devil
5. Unrefined metals
6. Box top
7. Exists
8. Tooth expert
9. Rip (apart)
10. Fairy-tale monster
11. "A rolling stone gathers no —"
16. Lose, as feathers
18. Dine
20. Extra tire
21. Store event
22. Teheran's land
23. Frees (of)
24. Petty quarrels
26. Dispatches
27. Debt notice
28. Great Lake
29. Jewels
31. Knife parts
35. Fountain favorite
36. Compass point
37. Baseball "four-bagger"
38. Chair or pew
39. Story
40. Largest continent
41. Traveled via horse
43. Use oars
44. —a chance!
45. Hint
46. Before: poetic
49. Scale tone

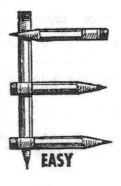

EASY

90 SPECIAL CHALLENGER CROSSWORD

"THE MAN'S NAME IS . . ."   by LOUIS SABIN

Here is a real toughie for you. We have omitted giving you such helps as "2 wds.," "hyph. wd.," and "slang"; but in the spirit of fair play, all abbreviations and foreign words are so indicated.

ACROSS

1. Splash gently
4. Assemble
8. Vend
12. Restrain
17. Help
19. Political columnist
21. Entreaty
22. Halos
23. Three Johns
27. Guess
28. Namesakes of an emperor
29. Dismal
30. Coin
31. Bastes
32. Cow-headed goddess
33. Tannery product
35. Isinglass
36. Pizza cooker
37. Novelist, Rita — Brown
40. Four more
45. Army subdivision
46. She: French
47. Costly
48. Upset
49. Gym cushion
50. Layered rock
52. Shabby
53. Photographer's request
54. Actor, Robert —
56. On the sheltered side
57. Teased
58. Two more

63. Arizonan Indian
66. 1948 Hitchcock film
67. Extorted
71. Habituate
72. Roof worker
73. Nails used as markers
75. Period of time
76. Prometheus' gift
77. Italian noble
78. New Testament letter: abbr.
79. Activate
80. Four more
86. Curved plank
87. Woman's name
88. Pick out
89. Diving birds
90. Sigher's word
91. Following
93. Choir voice
94. Salamanders
96. Stage section
97. Birds' perches
101. Three more
104. Debatable subject
105. Elite school
106. Chilling
107. Bruce, of "Coming Home"
108. Highlanders
109. Uncles: Scottish
110. Requirement
111. Suitable

DOWN

1. Intertwine

2. Arab robes
3. Saucy
4. French matrons: archaic
5. Cream
6. Medieval laborer
7. Boot section
8. Novelist, Muriel —
9. 1985 film, "St. — Fire"
10. Not as much
11. Fall back
12. Profession
13. Yokels
14. District
15. Impression
16. Sulky mood
18. Neptune's staff
20. Flair
24. Organic compound
25. Window decoration
26. "Ghosts" playwright
31. "Hamlet" or "Macbeth"
32. Pale color
33. Detecting device
34. Wed
35. Factory
36. Catapult
37. Boy Scout badge
38. Consecrate: archaic
39. Wrapped up
40. Unload
41. Wealth
42. Roman official
43. Hawaiian geese
44. Bounds

50. Barrel part
51. Water carrier
52. Archaeologist, at times
53. Surfeits
55. Timorous
57. Celtic star
59. Awn
60. Horse's turns
61. Swords
62. Flooded
63. Offends
64. Hamburger garnish
65. Make tracks
68. Dakotan Indian
69. Heiden and Clapton
70. Brunet
72. League members
73. Trail
74. Liquid measure
78. Cost
79. Darted
81. Fringed shoes
82. Efface
83. John Jacob —
84. So-called
85. Eminent
90. Shocking
91. Baldwin or Jonathan
92. Manumits
93. Nickname for a fairway legend
94. Certain shuttle operator: abbr.
95. See 108-Across
96. Husband of Lilith
97. Exhaust
98. Was obliged to
99. Land of the Incas
100. "Auld Lang —"
101. Musician's job
102. Strong alkali
103. Female lobster

91

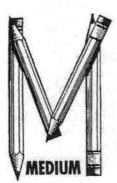

MEDIUM

ACROSS

1. Waterproof canvas
5. Space
9. Derby or bonnet
12. "Light bulb," in comics
13. Wrestling maneuvers
14. Mr. Lincoln, for short
15. Baseball's Craig —
17. Warning signal
19. Exist
20. Green gem
22. Long step
25. Raw minerals
26. Fuss: hyph. wd.
27. Emotionally intent
29. Do wrong
32. Whether — not
33. Smallest
36. Negative answer
37. Pod vegetable
39. Gentle
40. Rave
42. Rounded roof
44. Not dense
46. Sunburn result
49. Stern (of a ship)
50. E.T., for one
51. Scent
55. Five-dollar bill: slang
56. Inner "being"
58. Press (clothes)
59. Label
60. Completes
61. Arrive

DOWN

1. Pie plate
2. Summer drink
3. Hold back; hinder
4. Loyalist
5. Mimic
6. Ascend
7. Printer's measure
8. States
9. Annoy
10. Cain's brother
11. Take care of
16. Conducted
18. Make angry
21. Small motorcycles
22. Halt
23. Ripped (apart)
24. Ford and Pyle
28. Feel unwell
30. Taverns
31. Short message
34. Huge
35. Highway movement
38. Totaling
41. Conductor, — Toscanini
43. Half a pair
45. Golf course rating
46. Rubber boat
47. Producer Kazan
48. Potato
52. Overhead trains
53. Parent
54. Compass point
57. Atop

92

EASY

ACROSS

1. "Jabber"
4. Heap (on)
8. Mop, to a sailor
12. Historical period of time
13. Sour; tart
14. Tie, as for a shoe
15. Highly trained, as in a trade
17. Swiftness
18. Require
19. Huff and puff
20. Communion table
22. Most peppery
25. Ooze
26. Foundations
27. Sound from Santa
28. Flat cushion
29. Hits hard: slang
30. Cat's foot
31. "Santa Claus — Coming to Town"
32. Christmas postage stickers
33. In this place
34. Basements
36. More sensible
37. Dines
38. Blaze
39. Petty quarrels
41. Foretell
44. Relieve (a pain)
45. Highway
46. Corn spike
47. Picnic pests
48. Brink
49. Secret agent

DOWN

1. Of course!
2. Noah's boat
3. Applied enamel to
4. More ashen in color
5. Frosted (a cake)
6. Box top
7. Actor Asner
8. Inclines
9. Squander
10. Behave
11. Hive insect
16. Jump, frog style
17. Detests
19. Pillars
20. Jellied meat mold
21. Rental document
22. Corridors
23. Portion
24. — of Babel, Biblical structure
26. Chicago football team
29. Throbs
30. Cents
32. Blackboard materials
33. Difficult
35. Smallest amount
36. Soft leather
38. Boast
39. Mediterranean, for one
40. Skillet
41. Pea casing
42. Beanie or beret
43. Attempt
45. Do, —, mi

ACROSS

1. Joke
4. Eagle's claw
9. Cooking need
12. "Blessed — the meek . . ."
13. Not asleep
14. Regret
15. Halted
17. Milky
19. Marsh grass
20. Tinted
21. Senate runners
23. Most needy
26. Actor Estrada
27. Beach
28. Hello
29. Pekoe, for one
30. Heron's kin
31. Nourished
32. Indefinite article
33. Intends (to)
34. Mirth
35. City in Wyoming
37. Plant parts
38. Ireland, to poets
39. Have on
40. Become mature
42. Fate
45. Expert pilot
46. Conscious (of)
48. Expire
49. Coagulate
50. Start again
51. Likely

DOWN

1. Motorist's purchase
2. Skill
3. Atlanta's State
4. Records, in a way
5. Filled with wonder
6. Boy
7. All right
8. Empire State: 2 wds.
9. Group of lions
10. Umpire's call
11. Golfer's peg
16. Sneak a look
18. In this place
20. Portals
21. Flower part
22. Site of conflict
23. Bell's invention, for short
24. Piece of linen
25. Ocean movements
27. Blemish
30. Study group
31. Tallahassee's State
33. Foal's mother
34. Kid
36. Force back
37. Stitch again
39. Existed
40. Tattered cloth
41. Frozen water
42. Newsman Rather
43. Bite
44. Still
47. You and I

MEDIUM

94

HARD

ACROSS

1. Strong desire
7. Renter
13. Simpler
14. Slow: music
15. Sound of protest
16. Postal worker
18. Hartford's State: abbr.
19. Sheep's cry
21. Water vapor
22. The woman
23. Helps
25. Lubricate
26. Throat-clearing word
27. A judge of Israel
29. Decorate with raised designs
31. Actor Buttons
32. Rowing need
33. Scandinavian country
36. King's house
39. Inquisitive
40. Timetable abbreviation
42. Beneficiary
43. Mornings: abbr.
44. Teapot part
46. And not
47. Truck radio: abbr.
48. Removes impurities
50. Negative reply
51. System of self-defense
53. Wabble
55. Asserts
56. Robs

DOWN

1. Certain brew's sack
2. Nene's State
3. Exists
4. Edge
5. Oceans
6. Son of Poseidon
7. Mexican treat
8. A cheese
9. Woman's nickname
10. Chemical symbol for silver
11. Recesses
12. Indian symbols
17. Maui garland
20. Give a speech to
22. Reduce in length
24. Shabby
26. Disconcert
28. Lyric poem
30. Extinct bird
33. Between-meal treats
34. Burrowing marsupial
35. Italian port
36. Dressing bottles
37. A Barrymore
38. Mistakes
41. Decay
44. Locale
45. Waste allowance
48. Obese
49. Visualize
52. Egyptian sun god
54. Chemical symbol

ACROSS

1. Paving substance
4. Wingless insects
9. Time of day: abbr.
12. Fruit drink
13. Smallest amount
14. Battle
15. Auto fuel
16. Cereal grain
17. Prepared
19. Snare
21. Rip
22. Yell
24. Certain part of the week
27. Small pie
28. Glue
29. Perform (an act)
30. President Lincoln, for short
31. Harsh, dry coughs
32. Turf
33. Providence's State: abbr.
34. Armored vehicles
35. Certain
36. Zebra markings
38. Artist's stand
39. Swiss mountains
40. Sloped walkway
41. Nimble
43. Kind of fruit
44. Actress Gabor
47. Comic Aykroyd
48. Loop; slipknot
50. Food tin
51. Secret agent
52. Very thin; transparent
53. Powerful explosive

DOWN

1. Label
2. Woman's name
3. Return to original condition
4. Parade vehicle
5. Jump
6. Have lunch
7. While
8. Thoroughfares
9. Prize
10. Passing style
11. Attempt
18. Relieve
20. Wheel track
21. Elephants' teeth
22. Sky twinklers
23. Custom
24. Small nails
25. Idolize
26. Sing Swiss-style
28. Window squares
31. Occurs
32. Believe to be guilty
34. Money drawer
35. Detective Spade
37. Showery
38. Enthusiastic
40. Ascend
41. Commercials
42. Empty space
43. Enemy
45. Moving truck
46. Picnic pest
49. Cry of surprise

EASY

96

EASY

ACROSS

1. Mom's mate
4. Ringing sound
9. Put two and two together
12. Organ of hearing
13. Mississippi, for one
14. Spring month
15. Grand Canyon State
17. Angry
19. Sleeveless garment
20. Organs of smell
21. Lions' calls
23. Stoops
25. Aware of: slang
26. Went by bus
27. Behold!
29. High card
30. Shot (a gun)
31. Weaken
32. Myself
33. Not closed
34. Feminine name
35. Telegraphs
37. Desert animal
38. Bread serving
40. Golfer's cry
41. Walks in water
42. Sparkles
45. Dined
46. Real delight
48. Be in debt
49. Man's nickname
50. Oozes
51. Very small

DOWN

1. Pod vegetable
2. Paddle
3. Personal
4. Cranky; irritable
5. Yarn fluff
6. Actress Gardner
7. Compass point
8. Smiled broadly
9. Accumulate
10. Tropical fruit
11. Tints
16. Nothing
18. Fishing pole
21. Wander
22. "— upon a time . . ."
23. Dull people
24. Biblical garden
26. Ready for harvest
27. Country road
28. Semiprecious stone
30. Wooded areas
31. By an unknown means
34. Red planet
35. Make broader
36. Frozen water
37. Winter garments
38. Mop
39. Tardy
40. Envelope part
42. Lawyer's charge
43. Female sheep
44. Look at; view
47. Scale tone

97

MEDIUM

ACROSS

1. Applaud
5. Close noisily
9. Small, high plateau
13. Pack (away)
17. Dressing gown
18. Speed of running
19. Eager
20. Possess
21. Plentiful
23. Mean feeling
24. Cattle
25. Wager
26. Lyric poem
27. Drag
28. Charmingly old-fashioned
30. Smallest bill
31. Additional
32. Ringlet
33. Not fresh
36. Electric cord
37. Send out by radio
41. "On Golden —," movie
42. Auction
43. Chairs
44. One-spot card
45. "Who — you?"
46. Become weary
47. Ohio or Iowa
48. Magnet metal
49. Gives as compensation to
51. Some of them
52. Mix
53. Payable
54. Rubbish!: slang
55. Chum
56. Wear away
59. Stage accessories
60. Ogre
64. — of, frees from
65. Low-calorie regimens
66. Firm
67. Boulevard: abbr.
68. Commotion
69. Cash penalties
70. Roster
71. Not closed
72. Household employees
74. Sneak a look at
75. Current style
76. — and Andy, old-time radio favorites
77. Baseball sticks
78. Pastry dish
79. Ginger and clove
82. Circle segments
83. Forbid
84. Make lace
87. Molten rock
88. IRS investigation
90. Woo with music
92. Persia, nowadays
93. Secondhand
94. Suggest indirectly
95. — Alda, star of M*A*S*H
96. Camper's shelter
97. Thorny flower
98. Terminates
99. Jewels

DOWN

1. Crosspatch
2. Earring site
3. Border on
4. "Weapon" mightier than a sword
5. Digging tool
6. Country road
7. Behave
8. Part of us
9. Syrup-producing tree
10. Wicked
11. Take a chair
12. Enough
13. Shallow waters
14. Cab
15. Baking chamber
16. Traveled
22. Finished
23. Certain
27. — over, study closely
29. Footed vases
30. Elderly
31. 5,280 feet
32. Packing box
33. Ship's mast
34. Ripped
35. Once again
36. Armed conflicts
37. Taunt
38. Equine female
39. Sacred picture
40. Take care of
42. Cube's surface
43. Ceases
46. Factual
47. Seagoing vessels
48. Troubles
50. Totals (up)
51. Jogs
52. Musical group
54. Oak and willow
55. Harbor
56. Periods of time
57. Roller-coaster trip
58. Aroma
59. Two make a quart
60. False face
61. Record on cassette
62. Equally balanced
63. Split apart
65. Huge prehistoric reptile
66. Hastens
69. Musical TV series
70. Permits
71. Metallic rock
73. Empty

74. Treaty
75. Fork prong
77. Wedding "star"
78. Portions
79. Narrow opening
80. Peel

81. "— the Terrible," Russian czar
82. Fruit drinks
83. Twist
84. Story
85. First man

86. Wallet items
89. Army entertainers: abbr.
90. Transgression
91. Constantly scold
94. That boy

98

EASY

ACROSS

1. Faucet
4. Point a finger at
9. Health resort
12. Raw mineral
13. Enthusiastic
14. Track distance
15. For each
16. Hole in one
17. Lift (up)
19. Shoot (a gun)
21. Cooking fat
22. Use up, as money
24. Nippy; frosty
27. Need
28. Gales
29. Apiece: abbr.
30. Tiny insect
31. Metal tubes
32. Paving substance
33. Exist
34. Lucky number
35. Model-T man
36. Soft shoe
38. Yellowish metal
39. Dunks
40. Scornful sounds
41. Play division
43. Baltic or Red
44. Light brown
47. Pod vegetable
48. Prices
50. Biblical woman
51. Sure!
52. Commence
53. Large rodent

DOWN

1. Go one better than
2. "Where the Boys —," movie
3. Ideal
4. Goatee, for one
5. Fancy trim
6. Vital statistic
7. Part of "us"
8. Messenger chores
9. Playground chute
10. Daddies
11. Large primate
18. — and crafts
20. Writing fluid
21. Bedding
22. Bacon slices
23. TV discussion group
24. Windshield cleaner
25. Brings up, as a child
26. Fabric measures
28. Spouses
31. Salts' mates
32. Kitchen appliance
34. Washer cycle
35. To and —
37. Thoughts
38. Brag
40. Sudsy brew
41. Secret agent
42. Third letter
43. Depot: abbr.
45. Actress Gardner
46. Mesh trap
49. By

ACROSS

1. Fast plane
4. Slender
8. Constructed
12. Actress Gardner
13. N.Y. theater award
14. Prayer ending
15. Large, imposing house
17. Current style
18. Mooselike deer
19. Face part
20. Permitted by law
23. Long and thin
26. Egg-shaped
27. Wheel covering
28. — Paz, Bolivia
29. Beret, for one
30. Form
32. Movable cover
33. Paid notice
34. Daze
35. Information
36. Jungle cat
38. Pisa's lure
39. Small wagon
40. Dad's mate
41. On guard
43. Rings, watches and such
47. Drip
48. Foundation
49. Sight organ
50. Optical glass
51. Spoken
52. Obtain

DOWN

1. Fruity spread
2. Actress Gabor
3. Light brown
4. Motionless
5. Glance
6. Tavern
7. "— Blue Heaven"
8. Nautical
9. Revise, as a law
10. Cozy retreat
11. Finish
16. Tight closure
17. At that place
19. Cut off with scissors
20. Train making all stops
21. Dodge
22. Opening
23. Remain upright
24. Select group
25. "M*A*S*H" character
30. Begin
31. Injure
32. Ordinance
34. Glowing particles
35. Rounded roof
37. The Pacific, for one
38. Drying cloth
40. Small, high plateau
41. Entire amount
42. Robert E. —
43. Glass container
44. Table support
45. Cereal grain
46. Thus far
48. Actress Derek

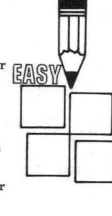

EASY

100

ACROSS

1. Daddies
4. Doughnut-shaped roll
9. Youngster
12. Octopus's protection
13. Worship
14. Country hotel
15. Revises
17. Metal container
18. Fishing aid
19. Petroleum
21. Border
23. Royal abodes
27. Slackened
30. Was indebted to
31. Wed
33. "City of Angels": abbr.
34. Melancholy
35. Takes pleasure in
36. Piece of soap
37. Musical tone
38. Discussion group
39. Appointment
40. Knight's horse
42. Harms
44. Boys
46. Still
47. Every one
49. Lamprey, for one
51. Flavor
55. Payment asked
56. Elevate
58. Feel poorly
59. "Sawbuck"
60. Direct the course of
61. Jewel

DOWN

1. Crusty dessert
2. Also
3. Glide over snow
4. Fundamental
5. Newspaper notice
6. Obtained
7. Cleveland's lake
8. Givers
9. Prongs
10. Single unit
11. Powerful explosive: abbr.
16. Frog's cousin
20. Tangy fruit
22. Happy
23. Fence supports
24. Expect
25. Guided
26. Rescued
28. Gladden
29. Challenges
32. Transmit (a message)
35. Climbing aids
36. Sack
38. Podded protein
39. Information
41. Actress Burstyn
43. Rhythm in verse
45. Bench
47. Toward the stern
48. Actor Marvin
50. Falsehood
52. Droop
53. Gift for Dad
54. Tall, hardy tree
57. Compass point

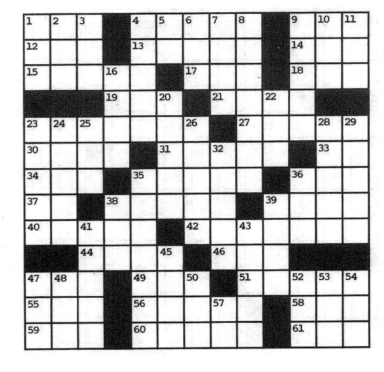

ACROSS

1. Type of beer
6. Central American Indian
11. Western State
12. Part of A.E.C.
14. Wicked
15. Synthetic fiber
17. Man's title: abbr.
18. Possessed
19. Style of jazz: hyph. wd.
20. Friar's title
21. Medical professional: abbr.
22. Temperate
23. Coagulate
24. Kitchen item
26. Playground feature
27. Match
28. Oil group: abbr.
29. Indicated
31. Glitter
34. Small equine
35. Football move
36. Woodman's tool
37. One of the March girls
38. Outward aspect
39. High explosive, for short
40. New England State: abbr.
41. Encircles
42. German river
43. Is worshipful
45. Idealized place
47. Black Sea city
48. Biblical man

DOWN

1. Mediterranean region
2. Greedy
3. Sal, for one
4. Man's nickname
5. Welsh dish
6. City official
7. At the apex
8. Hither's partner
9. Exist
10. Son of Cush
11. Indian leader
13. Packing box
16. Son of Adam
19. Petty officer
20. Movie: slang
22. Like January weather
23. Office worker
25. Dark wood
26. Blank area
28. Nocturnal marsupial
29. Ember
30. Southern dish
31. Coasted
32. Hawaiian porches
33. Additional
35. Sac
38. Young female pig
39. Record
41. Set
42. Distress call
44. Apiece: abbr.
46. As far as

101

102

ACROSS

1. Mr. Boone
4. Gift for a teacher
9. Single item
12. Do wrong
13. Ceiling opposite
14. 24 hours
15. Small vegetable
16. Small child
17. Marry secretly
19. Boat's company
21. Tallies
22. Car part
24. Berets, for example
25. Sailor's cry
26. Grottoes
27. Hello!
29. Title of respect
30. Ventured
31. Cushion
32. Boxing feat: abbr.
33. Employs
34. Make full
35. Social insects
36. Glue's kin
37. Blots
40. Desire
41. Very strong rope
42. Tilt
43. Possess
46. Everything
47. Elevate
49. Southern General
50. Golf mound
51. Very thin
52. Collection

DOWN

1. Energy
2. Exist
3. Farm implement
4. Behind
5. Make furrows
6. Cooking vessel
7. Behold!
8. Built
9. Fragrance
10. Back of the neck
11. Sight organs
18. Waste
20. Cowboy Rogers
21. Rescues
22. False face
23. Buckeye State
24. Rabbits' kin
26. Small wagons
27. Stop
28. Not busy
30. Big meals of the day
31. Small guns
33. Summon a taxi
34. Air cooler
36. Writing parchment
37. Shoo!
38. Story
39. Skilled
40. Knowing
42. Gift for Dad
44. Tiny
45. Mesh snare
48. Sigh of relief

ACROSS

1. Golf standard
4. Dishonor
9. Mao — Tung
12. Hockey surface
13. Aromatic wood
14. Have the flu, e.g.
15. Bothers
17. Grates
19. Cans
20. Lack
21. Opposite of "here"
23. Commandment breakers
26. Traveled on horseback
27. Auctioneer's cry
28. Speck
29. "I — Woman"
30. Most cherished
33. Close to
34. Encountered
36. Stone, Bronze, et al.
37. Shoe part
39. Printing machines
41. Remove soap from
42. Crazy: slang
43. Jargon
44. Sphere
46. Most hopeless
49. Breath
50. Pay hike
52. Regret
53. "— Miserables"
54. Use a rudder
55. Notice

DOWN

1. Small fruit seed
2. Highest card
3. Took a nap
4. Play division
5. Belonging to that woman
6. Public notices
7. Mrs. Kettle
8. Short, purposeful trips
9. Sampled (food)
10. Drink slowly
11. Certain city trains
16. Weary
18. Actress Jillian
20. Sly tricks
21. Hobo
22. "Iliad" author
23. Painful spots
24. Judicial garments
25. Fashion
27. Wise men
31. Spring holidays
32. Have an idea
35. Voices above baritones
38. Goes inside
40. Underwater ship, for short
41. Less common
43. Matter for a trial
44. Four quarts: abbr.
45. Fib
46. Dotted cube
47. Bring legal action against
48. Golf gadget
51. "One Day — a Time"

MEDIUM

104

ACROSS

1. Epoch
4. Long, heroic tale
8. Large boat
12. Brewer's tub
13. Tribe
14. O'Hara residence
15. Spielberg alien
16. "Skoal" and "cheers"
18. Crimson or scarlet
19. Excuse
21. Helpful hint
23. Chart
24. Observed
26. Palmetto State: abbr.
28. Ale's kin
30. "Lucky" number
31. Mate for Ma
32. — Tin Tin
33. Chirp
34. Brooch
35. Either
36. Make butter
37. Sharpen
38. Us
39. Cereal grains
40. Marry
41. Mr. Selleck
42. Autumn, for one
45. Fuss
47. Placard
50. Myself
51. Finished
53. Peruse
54. Stinging insect
55. Action
56. Corn units
57. Conclude

DOWN

1. Always
2. Classify
3. By
4. Ice cream serving
5. Actor Alda
6. Car fuel
7. Picnic pest
8. Holy one: abbr.
9. Angel's "instrument"
10. Anger
11. Cushion
16. Russian ruler
17. Like a cliff
20. Prayer ending
22. Rustic travel stop
24. Prophets
25. Level
26. Twirl
27. Walking stick
28. Forehead
29. Ireland
30. Close
33. Winner, for short
34. Vegetable shells
36. Dove call
37. Listen
40. Unwanted plants
41. Musical sound
42. Constellation part
43. Portent
44. Require
45. Do sums
46. Stag's mate
48. Mine deposit
49. Red or Baltic
52. Mr. Sullivan
54. Beatles tune, "Let It —"

EASY

ACROSS

1. Ancient Philistine city
5. Upsurge
9. Darrow's forte
12. Selves
13. Writer Gardner
14. According to: 2 wds.
15. Reviewing: 3 wds.
18. Take steps
19. Rocky's friend, Apollo —
20. "Swedish Nightingale" Lind
23. Stratagem
25. Greenland colonizer
26. Fish sauce
27. Homeless exiles: abbr.
30. Play second fiddle: 4 wds.
33. Wind direction: abbr.
34. Carnegie or Georgia —
35. Fitzgerald or Raines
36. Diminutive word ending
37. Exotic
38. Nimble
41. Only
42. Vacillates: 3 wds.
48. Naval rating: abbr.
49. Stamped (on)
50. Snoop
51. Japanese coin
52. Bastes
53. Terminal access

DOWN

1. Thicken
2. Past
3. Animal enclave
4. Sidewise
5. Holy season
6. Unit of work
7. Clerical garment
8. Ultimate preener
9. "Dagwood" portrayer
10. Lily plant
11. Scepter
16. Unfriendly
17. Clamor (for)
20. Gastineau's teammates
21. Time periods
22. Goddess of victory
23. Recognize
24. Solidarity's Walesa
26. Encourage a felon
27. Pastrami purveyor, for short
28. Ashen
29. He was "the man"
31. Bears witness
32. Persuading
36. Wapiti
37. An NBC sitcom
38. Fundamentals
39. Yawn
40. Sacred image
41. Says further
43. Exist
44. PDQ
45. Mauna —
46. WWII assault craft: abbr.
47. Go steady with

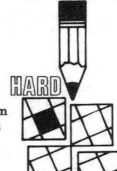

HARD

by RUSS CARLEY

Bible references in this puzzle are from the King James Version. You'll find it stimulating to solve, and may discover you know more about the Bible than you think you do.

ACROSS

1. The blind and dumb both spake and —. *Matt. 12:22*
4. The —r that killeth any person . . . may flee. *Josh. 20:3*
9. Be not — from me; for trouble is near. *Ps. 22:11*
12. Chief officer of David
13. A land flowing with milk and —
14. I say the truth . . . I — not. *Rom. 9:1*
15. One witness shall not — against any person. *Num. 35:30*
17. Great is your r— in heaven. *Matt. 5:12*
19. Go to the —, thou sluggard. *Prov. 6:6*
20. Biblical kingdom
21. I . . . — mine head at you. *Job 16:4*
24. O thou — among women, go thy way. *Song 1:8*
27. We spend our years as a — that is told. *Ps. 90:9*
28. The — make their nests. *Ps. 104:17*
29. He maketh me — lie down in green pastures. *Ps. 23:2*
30. I will also — of you one question. *Mark 11:29*
31. The children of Israel shall pitch their —. *Num. 1:52*
32. — many loaves have ye? *Mark 8:5*
33. Ye shall not eat of — . . . lest ye die. *Gen. 3:3*
34. He shall give thee the de— of thine heart. *Ps. 37:4*
35. Precept must be upon precept . . . — upon line. *Isa. 28:10*
36. Jacob's thigh was out of joint, as he w— with him. *Gen. 32:25*
38. Fill the waterpots with —. *St. John 2:7*
39. They — their peace. *Mark 3:4*
40. Set them in two rows, six on a —. *Lev. 24:6*
41. The Holy Ghost descended in a bodily — like a dove. *Luke 3:22*
43. They . . . slew seventy —. *II Ki. 10:7*
47. A woman . . . touched the — of his garment. *Matt. 9:20*
48. The treaders shall — out no wine. *Isa. 16:10*
50. One — is past . . . there come two woes more. *Rev. 9:12*
51. How long will it be — thou be quiet? *Jer. 47:6*
52. They wash not their — when they eat. *Matt. 15:2*
53. What mean these seven — lambs? *Gen. 21:29*

DOWN

1. Make them — down. *Luke 9:14*
2. Blessed — the pure in heart. *Matt. 5:8*
3. There — no room for them in the inn. *Luke 2:7*
4. His face did — as the sun. *Matt. 17:2*
5. The —y city, he layeth it low. *Isa. 26:5*
6. Is — thing too hard for the Lord? *Gen. 18:14*
7. Why are — fearful? *Matt. 8:26*
8. On my — is the shadow of death. *Job 16:16*
9. His eyes were as a — of fire. *Rev. 1:14*
10. Behold the fowls of the —. *Matt. 6:26*
11. By faith they passed through the — sea as by dry land. *Heb. 11:29*

16. Thou shalt not — the name of the Lord . . . in vain. *Ex. 20:7*

18. Ye shall hear of — and rumours of wars. *Matt. 24:6*

20. I will harden the h— of the Egyptians. *Ex. 14:17*

21. He . . . went up the —s thereof. *Ezek. 40:6*

22. Make speed, —, stay not. *I Sam. 20:38*

23. They shall w— with me . . . for they are worthy. *Rev. 3:4*

24. I . . . will refine them as silver is re—. *Zech. 13:9*

25. There shall not be left one — upon another. *Luke 21:6*

26. The — of Babel

28. The well . . . is between Kadesh and —. *Gen. 16:14*

31. He that — his land shall have plenty of bread. *Prov. 28:19*

32. The archers — him; and he was sore wounded. *I Sam. 31:3*

34. There is but a — between me and death. *I Sam. 20:3*

35. They shall keep my — and my statutes. *Ezek. 44:24*

37. I write not these things to — you. *I Cor. 4:14*

38. These are the — which I spake. *Luke 24:44*

40. No man was . . . worthy to open and to — the book. *Rev. 5:4*

41. — brought forth her firstborn son. *Luke 2:7*

42. His wife was of the daughters of Aaron, and — name was Elisabeth. *Luke 1:5*

43. I will not with ink and — write unto thee. *III John 13*

44. — no man any thing, but to love one another. *Rom. 13:8*

45. Behold, — is the accepted time. *II Cor. 6:2*

46. One thing I know, that, whereas I was blind, now I —. *St. John 9:25*

49. The name of the elder was Leah . . . the younger was —chel. *Gen. 29:16*

The following two Diagramlesses have been started for you to give you your initial clues. Use both the definitions and the definition numbers as aids in supplying the words and the black squares to go into the diagram. Remember, the pattern of black squares is symmetrical. The example below shows the meaning of symmetry of the black squares in the diagram. When you have discovered the correct placement of a black square, its mate can be inserted in a corresponding position on the opposite side of the diagram.

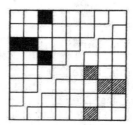

ACROSS

1. High Swiss mountain
4. Post-office purchase
9. Watched the neighbor's kids
12. Ocean
13. Panama or Erie —
14. Falsehood
15. Gather (crops)
17. Oak-tree nut
19. Cistern
20. Quit
21. Get up
23. Rags
26. Musical sound
27. Hibernators' retreats
28. Cry of surprise
29. Pull hard
30. Pastry chef
31. Hint
32. That thing
33. Tiny skin openings
34. Box
35. Basements
37. Silly blunder: slang
38. "As — as pie"
39. Bank offering
40. Civil War commander
42. Moves fast, as a horse
45. TV show, "— House"
46. Choose by vote
48. Snooze
49. Cozy room
50. Rounded roofs
51. Foxy

DOWN

1. Fire residue
2. Meadow: poetic
3. Leaving
4. Act division
5. Duty
6. Unwanted picnic visitor
7. Mother
8. Large serving dish
9. Incline
10. Breeze
11. Half a score
16. Flower holder
18. Portable beds
20. Rescues
21. Loft
22. Way
23. Grasps

24. Awaken
25. See-through, as fabric
27. Tote
30. Bragged
31. Large, mounted guns
33. Scheme
34. Kind of fuel
36. Gain knowledge
37. Metal fasteners
39. Wedding-gown trimming
40. Idol
41. Regret
42. Sapphire or emerald
43. Buddy
44. Secret agent
47. — and behold

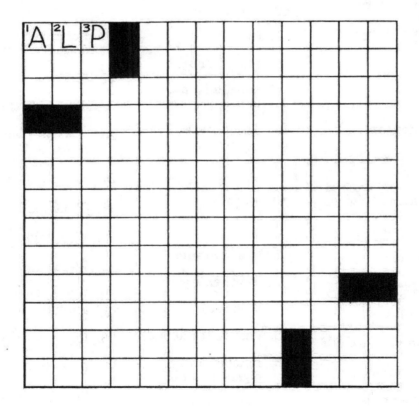

This Diagramless is 15 boxes wide by 15 boxes deep.

ACROSS

1. Fasten

4. Smell

6. Arrow propeller

9. Rounded roof

10. Ocean's rise and fall

11. — Vegas

12. Defied

13. Relies (upon)

15. From midnight to midnight

18. Shaving hazards

19. Judicious

20. Swifter

23. Righetti and Winfield, for short

24. Rub with a cloth

25. Vermilion

27. Dollar bills

28. Muscular power

29. Debated

31. Metal sources

32. Less worthy

34. Plot of flowers

35. Made fresh again

37. Castles' protective ditches

38. Go astray

40. Otherwise

41. Rip

43. Woven snare

44. Long, adventurous tale

45. Encountered

DOWN

1. Pea container

2. Heathen's god

3. Wanderer

5. Feel bitter about

6. Finches and pigeons, et al.

7. Lyric poems of tribute

8. Join in marriage

10. Large storage container

12. Diminishes

14. Wharf

15. Supped

16. Inquires

17. "Certainly!"

19. Become dimmer

20. Penalized with a cash retribution

21. Simians

22. Join with thread

23. "— can't win them all!"

24. Telephone cable

26. Sketched

28. Weep aloud

30. Welcomes

32. Large, four-footed animal

33. Pay one's share

35. Function

36. Slumbertime vision

37. Males

39. Intense anger

42. Rodent

by TED SHANE

You'll find zany definitions in this crossword by Ted Shane, so please look out for traps. For example, the definition for 30-Across is "Ocean-going flappers," and the answer is GULLS. The clues are sly, so be careful.

ACROSS

1. What candy is for children
7. What teen-agers do standing up
13. This little thing caused a war between Florida and California
14. Home of the brave
15. If this goes on it will come to nothing
16. Hit below the belt in the battle of youth vs. old age
17. *Hymenoptera picnickibus*
18. A kind of marine chor
19. A bloomin' backward little thing
21. They get into lots of pickles, and get pickled themselves
23. Colt and dolt!
24. Bad Biblical bargainer
26. Bobbed tail
27. Fly like a flea
28. Now Available: 1-rm phone booths, upper or lower orange crate, broom closet in 1/2-rm. apt.
30. Ocean-going flappers
31. Aren't these kerchoo kerchiefs tearable?
33. Kind of tooth that may send you to the dentist
36. Some people think this is all there is to a quarrel: 2 wds.
40. Whar she blows for whalers
41. This little devil got in the back way
42. Wherewithal for knit-wits' tall tales
43. This fresh thing has never been in the subway
44. Merry, Endurable, Encorporated Corn-on-the-cob Eaters
46. Charter member of the horsey set
47. The first and last of any loan
48. Almost noon
49. What a man born in B. C. would be today
51. A piece of pie
52. Cutup on many TV shows
54. Impossible present tense of redden
56. Leg gear
57. Human, isn't it?

DOWN

1. This has caused considerable amazement
2. Administer an eye-opener
3. You're probably right here right now: abbr.
4. Sales slogan for this item: "Business always booming"
5. Pretty rough talk for an old-timer
6. What no men are filled with

7. Ox box
8. They've been scratching out an existence for years at the post office and should retire
9. As a matter of flax, it's the same old soak
10. Another ology
11. Game animal
12. Snappy glass eyes; makes contacts; are followed by quick developments
20. The first part of any banquet
22. Re Paris styles: Stop, Look and —
23. American football team
25. Kind of nonsense
27. Kind of person who watches his p's and q's and i's and t's
29. A-1 tea is sipped on this isle
30. What people filled with 1-Down usually say
32. Horse with a radiator cap
33. He was a world-famous Georgian
34. Say it in a neigh-borly way
35. Corny type of listener
37. It takes this John an eon to part with his pennies
38. A very goods man in England
39. It has a lot of pull
41. Hands across the border
44. Nightly follower
45. Lamb's tales were his specialty
48. Kind of phyte
50. Don't Drink This
53. Backward lieutenant: abbr.
55. First thing to see in Dublin

110

ACROSS

1. Was introduced to
4. Disgrace
9. Weep out loud
12. "We — Family"
13. Records on cassettes
14. Actor's signal
15. Get ready
17. Shipping box
19. Dollar bill
20. Furnace fuel
21. Burn with hot water
24. Right; proper
27. Highway "tax"
28. Blackboard
29. Informal greeting
30. Bullring cheer
31. Steamship, tug, etc.
32. Label
33. Baton Rouge's State: abbr.
34. Farm buildings
35. Misplace
36. Landed properties
38. Silly mistake: slang
39. — and crafts
40. Female chicken
41. Get up
43. Perils
47. Moving truck
48. Circular
50. By way of
51. Colony-dwelling insect
52. Loses fur
53. Omelet basis

DOWN

1. Geographical chart
2. Make a 38-Across
3. Golf peg
4. Band platform
5. Jack rabbit
6. Gorilla
7. Myself
8. Accompanies
9. Climb, as a mountain
10. Not at home
11. Stinging insect
16. Opinion survey
18. Uncommon
20. Paint layers
21. "Swiped"
22. Certain soft drinks
23. Malt drink
24. Tribal groups
25. Pursue
26. Striped feline
28. "Boo-boos"
31. Pitchers' opponents
32. 2,000 pounds
34. Prohibits
35. Actress, Shelley —
37. Contaminate; spoil
38. Makes curved
40. Clock part
41. Actress Gardner
42. Campaigned for office
43. Scheduled to arrive
44. Night before a holiday
45. Trucker's tractor
46. Droop
49. Cry of surprise

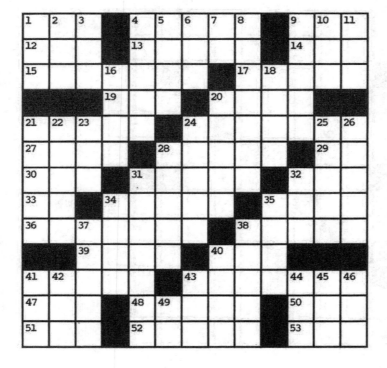

ACROSS

1. Electrical unit, for short
4. Neckwear
9. Stitch
12. Zodiac lion
13. Linger
14. —-la-la
15. The "Sunshine State"
17. Pizza's "home"
19. Completed
20. Traps
21. Actress Struthers
23. "Casablanca" star's nickname
24. Yuletide song
25. Archetype
26. Proceed
28. — and outs
29. Leafy greens
30. Damage
31. Gym class: abbr.
32. Slices open
33. Bargain
34. Property claims
35. Warsaw residents
36. Declares
38. Spoken
39. Fresh, as celery
40. Mountain scaled by Hillary
43. Belonging to us
44. Prankish sprites
46. Sailor
47. Actor Craven
48. Lion's sounds
49. Secret agent

DOWN

1. F.D.R. opponent Landon
2. Tillis or Torme
3. Curly-haired dogs
4. Glossy
5. System of symbols
6. Ms. Gardner
7. In reference to
8. Decorated with a thread-like edging
9. Gaze intently
10. Writer Stanley Gardner
11. Methods
16. Throw (dice)
18. Peacock's pride
20. Bubbly drinks
21. Cut
22. First-rate: 2 wds.
23. Runs suddenly
25. Large water pipes
26. Strong wind
27. Mined minerals
29. Woody Allen's "sci-fi" hit
30. Wooden-headed hammers
32. Occupies a seat
33. Glide
34. Dens
35. Squeeze
36. Flat-bottomed boat
37. Accurate
38. Finished
40. Zsa Zsa's sis
41. Tree fluid
42. Attempt
45. — and behold

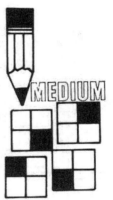

MEDIUM

112

ACROSS

1. Siamese or tabby
4. Miami tree
8. Go to the mall
12. This land: abbr.
13. Out
14. Shade
15. Word groups
17. H$_2$O
18. Possessive word
19. Fishing cord
20. Chinese bear
23. Question-type jokes
26. Woe!
27. Keeps
28. Musical note
29. A Reiner
30. Interlaced
31. Move, as a dog's tail
32. At home
33. Store transactions
34. Go out with
35. Area
37. Combines
38. Fedora and derby
39. Sing without words
40. Boasts
42. Routs
46. Soothe
47. Girl-chaser
48. Use a straw
49. Ogles
50. Stops
51. Lock opener

DOWN

1. Saucer's "mate"
2. Fire residue
3. Driveway sealer
4. Fettuccine, for one
5. Overwhelms
6. — Vegas
7. Song, "— Funny Valentine"
8. Gets up
9. Tourist stop
10. Small bill
11. For each
16. Helps
17. Add breadth to
19. Resides
20. Fashion capital
21. Unaccompanied
22. Catch
23. Black bird
24. Overjoy
25. Wise men
27. Flies alone
30. Lingers
31. Wane's opposite
33. Theater platforms
34. Small coin
36. Hurry after
37. Old-time hand warmers
39. Clutched
40. Spelling contest
41. Actor Milland
42. Put on
43. Invite
44. Bind
45. Secret agent
47. "In God — Trust"

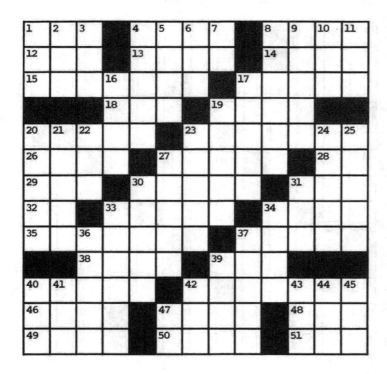

ACROSS

1. "Con" games: slang
6. Underpinning
11. Military nucleus
12. Nabs
14. Crop up
15. Muezzin's tower
16. Forest mom
17. Duet's lead
19. Mr. Parseghian
20. Give the cold shoulder
22. Border agency: abbr.
23. Lode
24. Bullets: slang
26. Flared trousers
27. Wind-blown sand heaps
29. The South
30. Of punishment
31. Brobdingnagian
32. Milky semiprecious stone
33. Barker or Newhart
34. Sprint
38. Mother hog
39. Initially
41. Adversary
42. Steinbeck's "— With Charley"
44. Courtroom excuse
46. Offbeat
47. Peels
48. Perceive
49. Put into use

DOWN

1. Oodles
2. Actress, Leslie —
3. So long!
4. Mr.'s mate
5. Leak slowly
6. Edges
7. Cartoonist, Peter —
8. Sargasso or Red
9. Sabra
10. Antiseptic
12. Kind of acid
13. Laurel and Kenton
18. Backboard attachments
21. Trite
23. Bothered
25. "The Velvet Fog," to friends
26. See 31-Across
27. Banishes
28. Not conscious (of)
29. Rerecords
30. Guards' stations
31. Trigger or Mr. Ed
33. Bosh: slang
35. Blazing
36. Solemn
37. Robbery: slang
39. Bogs
40. Word with "deck" or "measure"
43. Moving truck
45. Not strict

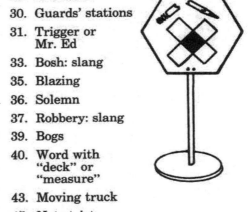

HARD

113

114

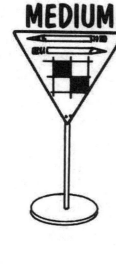

MEDIUM

ACROSS

1. For each
4. Certain cuts of meat
9. Amazing!
12. "The Greatest"
13. Lift with a pulley
14. Ms. Gardner
15. "—, Row the Boat Ashore"
17. Talked wildly
19. Requiring great effort
20. Angler's gear
21. Get going
23. Transmits
24. Restore to health
25. Unexpected difficulties
26. Deputy: abbr.
28. "Pride — Prejudice," Austen novel
29. Push roughly
30. Pod "resident"
31. Mexico's continent: abbr.
32. Test grade
33. Mr. Alda
34. Extra
35. Candid
36. Bring into being
38. Adolescent
39. Essence; vital part
40. Put in order
43. Have lunch
44. Actress Barkin
46. Long, long time
47. Football scores: abbr.
48. Actors' parts
49. See 20-Across

DOWN

1. Actress Dawber
2. Yale athlete
3. Fitness guru Simmons
4. Map
5. Used a gardening tool
6. Lubricate
7. Letter addition: abbr.
8. Unfamiliar
9. Ocean ridges
10. Above
11. Rolls of money
16. Rabbit relative
18. Totals (up)
20. Interlace
21. Glance at quickly
22. Food fish
23. Sleep noisily
25. Coastline
26. Rely (on)
27. Armored vehicle
29. Strew
30. Schedule-maker
32. Mast
33. Region
34. Acts as an usher
35. Fronded plants
36. Guitarist Atkins
37. Peruse
38. Oak or elm
40. Every single one
41. Sticky substance: slang
42. Conclusion
45. — and behold!

ACROSS

1. Bread spread
4. Tranquil
8. Large quantity
12. Ms. Gardner
13. Operatic solo
14. Fishing stick
15. Considered
17. Allay
18. Common preposition
19. Renowned
20. Agreement
22. Burghoff role
25. Get up
27. Food fish
28. Health club
31. Ocean
32. Road
34. Body joint
35. Expose to the sun
36. Informer: slang
37. Hum monotonously
39. Jabs
41. Assert
42. After a while
45. Window glass
47. Prophetic sign
48. Drips
52. Transmit
53. Grow dim
54. Epoch
55. Terminates
56. Is in debt
57. Arid

DOWN

1. Container for 1-Across
2. Hail!
3. Wizard
4. Shopper's vehicle
5. Eagerness
6. Falsehood
7. Insane
8. Lance
9. Rich soil
10. Otherwise
11. Unwanted plant
16. Picnic pests
19. Lost color
20. Ago
21. Region
23. Sharp
24. Speck
26. Mistake
28. Removed snow, in a way
29. Evergreen
30. Imitator
33. Acorn producer
38. Bad-smelling
39. Awaits decision
40. Backbone
42. Misplace
43. Prayer ending
44. Look after
46. High cards
48. "Tea for —"
49. Uncooked
50. Blunder
51. Utter

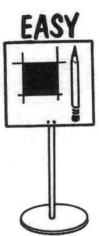

EASY

ACROSS

1. Retreated (with "back")
5. Damage; spoil
8. Get ready (for)
12. Jai —
13. Mimic
14. "Leo's" sound
15. Spice for apple pie
17. Otherwise
18. Football move
19. "Arthur" star Moore
21. Compass point
22. TV pioneer Arnaz
23. Actor Holbrook
25. Cornfield sight
30. Lily plant
32. Fib
33. TV actress Copley
34. Famous feuders
37. Decimal point
38. Wear out, as cuffs
39. Paddle
41. Vocation
44. Legendary figure, Paul —
47. Actor Roberts
48. 30th U.S. President
50. Bits of fluff
51. Ornamental vase
52. Chair
53. Young fellows
54. Golf peg
55. Is mistaken

DOWN

1. Truth
2. Director Kazan
3. Knight of the Round Table
4. Chain parts
5. Flamboyant fictional aunt
6. Part of a military address: abbr.
7. Gave, as for approval
8. Foretell
9. Bread-basket item
10. Comfort
11. Quarry
16. Pub drinks
20. Employ
22. Occurring every 24 hours
23. Cry of triumph
24. Southern State: abbr.
26. Distinct: hyph. wd.
27. Comic-book character: 2 wds.
28. Gold: Spanish
29. Humor
31. Results
35. Wrath
36. Spiritual force
40. Fragrant seed
41. Battery compartment
42. Pavarotti's specialty
43. Thick peel
44. Rib, for one
45. Seaweed product
46. Trawls
49. Mined substance

ACROSS

1. Watch face
5. Engrossed
9. Matterhorn, e.g.
12. Assumed function
13. Charles Lamb's alias
14. Green legume
15. Coldhearted
18. County seat of Somerset
19. Most positive
22. Staid
26. In the manner of: 2 wds.
27. At any time: poet.
29. Hypothetical force
30. Awareness
34. Claw
35. Shopkeeper's agency: abbr.
36. Warm season: French
37. Melodious
40. Certain pachyderms
42. French bacteriologist
44. Silent: 4 wds.
50. Us: German
51. Sponsorship: var. sp.
52. Bismarck's State: abbr.
53. "— the ramparts"
54. Slight hollow
55. Harness for oxen

DOWN

1. Thick: French
2. Charged atom
3. Hirt and Jolson
4. Philippine island
5. Distinctions
6. Author Paton
7. Actress Zasu
8. Lake —, western resort
9. Fitting
10. Oahu garland
11. High moccasin
16. Radiation emitter
17. Concluded
19. Spa feature
20. Of a forearm bone
21. Circle "spokes"
23. E.T., e.g.
24. Silverheels role
25. Moves gradually
28. Football positions: abbr.
31. Abscond
32. Side by side
33. Old Testament book
38. Full
39. Siouan Indian
41. Subtle sarcasm
43. Chinese dynasty
44. Quid pro —
45. French article
46. Jerusalem resident: abbr.
47. Japanese salad plant
48. Egyptian cotton
49. Supplement

HARD

118

E A S Y

ACROSS

1. High mountain
4. Gable or Bogart
9. Dairy animal
12. Eff follower
13. Car's stopping device
14. Actress Gardner
15. Strange
16. Rowing need
17. Long, slender candle
19. Tom-tom or bongo
21. Warning signals
22. Distribute
24. Shapes
25. Marsh grass
26. Exaggerated stories
27. "I've Gotta — Me"
29. Hearing organ
30. Manicuring tools
31. Ocean
32. One
33. Rings slowly, as a bell
34. Church service
35. Pilgrim Standish
36. Birthday celebration
37. Overflows
39. Tie
40. Howdy!
41. Skillet
42. Anger
45. Furniture wood
46. In what place
48. Immediately
49. Snoop
50. Saturates
51. Needle hole

DOWN

1. In the past
2. Guided
3. Door-to-door salesman
4. Approximately
5. Stuff
6. Paving substance
7. All right
8. Goes to bed
9. Sleeveless garments
10. Baking need
11. Battles
18. Battle weapons
20. Fishing pole
21. Shoe bottoms
22. Region
23. Thin
24. Drops
26. Roofing squares
27. Defeat
28. Simple
30. Comes after
31. "Crowded" fish
33. Cultivate
34. " — of La Mancha," play
35. The galaxy's — Way
36. Yearns (for)
37. Store
38. Bell-shaped fruit
39. Tree-trunk cover
41. Pod vegetable
43. Cowboy Rogers
44. Female sheep
47. Cry of surprise

ACROSS

1. Race-track circuit
4. Snare
8. Word of woe
12. Actress, — Marie Saint
13. Cavity
14. Flooring substance
15. Tanned, as skin
17. Loyal
18. Goals
19. Reveries
21. Dipper
23. Alda or Arkin
24. Depraved
25. Revising
29. Call for help
30. Tennis great, Chris —
31. Shoe part
32. Adds sugar to
34. Post-Mardi gras period
35. Dresses in
36. Ten-cent pieces
37. Cutting down grain
40. Short skirt
41. Heroic poem
42. Scrooge's given name
46. Portable shelter
47. Undercooked
48. Id's partner
49. Fragments
50. Doer: suffix
51. Corporal's boss: abbr.

DOWN

1. Ushered
2. Actress Gardner
3. Heavenly place
4. Short essay
5. Actors Howard and Moody
6. Tavern drink
7. Bicycle riders, e.g.
8. Be present at
9. Italian "dollar"
10. Former college attendee
11. Understands
16. Destroy
20. Talk loudly
21. Minus
22. Acknowledge
23. Prayer closings
25. Vindicators
26. Tax-form verb
27. "— But the Brave"
28. Obtains
30. Famed British prep school
33. Court orders
34. Demarcation
36. 1982 movie/meeting place
37. Allot
38. Candid
39. Air current
40. Nothing more than
43. Home-run aid
44. Omelet ingredient
45. Decompose

120

HARD

ACROSS

1. Exclamation of triumph
4. Unspoken
9. Limb
12. Before now
13. Actress — Massey
14. Born
15. Leisurely walk
17. Commonplace
19. Give sparingly (with "out")
20. Actor Finney
21. Gleam
23. Dakota Indian
24. Window glass
25. Check the books
26. River in Italy
28. Boxing great
29. Avarice
30. Chicago ballplayer
31. Japanese drama
32. Quarrels
33. Golfer's warning
34. Perhaps
35. Truck, in Leeds
36. Black Sea port
38. Alda or Ladd
39. Sample
40. Put an end to
43. " — A Wonderful Life," film
44. Football forerunner
46. British miler
47. Declare
48. Velocity
49. Shade tree

DOWN

1. Owns
2. Turkish title
3. Stage magician
4. Deed
5. Toward shelter
6. Remove errors from: abbr.
7. Currently fashionable
8. Sensational newspaper
9. Append
10. Elevate
11. Dissolve
16. Not any
18. Border (on)
20. Assistants
21. Nine inches
22. Angel's headgear
23. Soft leather
25. Netherlands Antilles island
26. Sound of contentment
27. Be guided by
29. Yellowstone Park features
30. Wall molding
32. Rapid
33. Young horse
34. Untidy
35. Politician Bentsen
36. Singer Redding
37. Information
38. French cleric
40. Mature
41. Sun god
42. Haw's partner
45. Out of bed

ACROSS

1. Devotee
4. "Aida" or "Carmen"
9. Dads
12. Chilly cube
13. Hay bundles
14. Feel poorly
15. Wobbles
17. Word of repentance
19. Student furniture
20. Chaste
21. Untrue
23. Sun umbrella
26. Aid's "pal"
27. Roll with a hole
28. Scale note
29. "My Country — of Thee"
30. Sounds
31. Little drink
32. Mr. Asner
33. Some carpets
34. Plunge into water
35. Those owing
37. Desert animal
38. Praise
39. Toasty
40. Pop singer
42. Game with a prize
45. Skillet
46. Listened to
48. Regret
49. Plus
50. Late
51. Envision

DOWN

1. Proper
2. High card
3. Pine features
4. Fat
5. Recreation area
6. Overhead trains
7. It follows "do"
8. Guarantees
9. Peels
10. Broadcast
11. Crafty
16. 18-Down is one kind
18. Spoken
20. Book leaves
21. Destined
22. Hymn, "— With Me"
23. Twinges
24. Oil fruit
25. Boutoniere site
27. Plank
30. Idea; notion
31. Cooks on low heat
33. Kenton or Laurel
34. Dash around
36. Unseeing
37. Sweet treats
39. Sentence unit
40. Baden, for one
41. Light brown
42. Auto
43. Take to court
44. It follows "ess"
47. Apiece: abbr.

MEDIUM

BIBLE CROSSWORD **MEDIUM**

by **RUSS CARLEY**

Bible references in this puzzle are from the King James Version. You'll find it stimulating to solve, and may discover you know more about the Bible than you think you do.

ACROSS

1. I will — you out of . . . bondage. *Ex. 6:6*
4. And there were in the — country shepherds. *Luke 2:8*
8. Thy kingdom —. Thy will be done. *Matt. 6:10*
12. If we love — another, God dwelleth in us. *I John 4:12*
13. Thine is . . . the power, and the glory, for ever. —. *Matt. 6:13*
14. God shall wipe — all tears. *Rev. 7:17*
15. I — no pleasant bread. *Dan. 10:3*
16. Go into the wilderness to — Moses. *Ex. 4:27*
17. On the seventh day God —d his work. *Gen. 2:2*
18. They bind me fast with new —. *Judg. 16:11*
20. I will give unto thee the — of the kingdom of heaven. *Matt. 16:19*
22. Is any thing — hard for the Lord? *Gen. 18:14*
24. Moses — up the tabernacle. *Ex. 40:18*
28. He calleth together his — and neighbours. *Luke 15:6*
32. Sailors, and as many as — by sea, stood afar off. *Rev. 18:17*
33. He that hath an —, let him hear. *Rev. 2:7*
34. They brought —iel, and cast him into the den of lions. *Dan. 6:16*
36. Divided the Red — into parts. *Ps. 136:13*
37. There — a great storm of wind. *Mark 4:37*
40. The Lord himself shall — from heaven. *I Thess. 4:16*
43. They rose up before Moses . . . men of —. *Num. 16:2*

45. — can forgive sins, but God alone? *Luke 5:21*
46. No man was found worthy . . . to — the book. *Rev. 5:4*
48. Be strengthened with might by his Spirit in the — man. *Eph. 3:16*
52. He shall shave all his — off his head. *Lev. 14:9*
55. Why beholdest thou the — . . . in thy brother's eye? *Matt. 7:3*
57. — no man any thing, but to love one another. *Rom. 13:8*
58. Simon, (whom he — named Peter). *Luke 6:14*
59. Deliver us from —. *Matt. 6:13*
60. The — Commandments
61. Cain . . . — his brother. *I John 3:12*
62. I will not — them away fasting. *Matt. 15:32*
63. Take heed l— any man deceive you. *Mark 13:5*

DOWN

1. They shall — like young lions. *Isa. 5:29*
2. John was cast — prison. *Matt. 4:12*
3. God caused a — sleep to fall upon Adam. *Gen. 2:21*
4. — and Delilah
5. Herod . . . heard of the f— of Jesus. *Matt. 14:1*
6. Blessed are the —: for they shall inherit the earth. *Matt. 5:5*
7. Pray, lest ye — into temptation. *Mark 14:38*
8. Render to — the things that are Caesar's. *Mark 12:17*
9. Jesus Christ . . . washed us from our sins in his — blood. *Rev. 1:5*
10. I am not — . . . but speak forth the . . . truth. *Acts 26:25*

11. An — for an eye, and a tooth for a tooth. *Matt. 5:38*

19. What shall I do that I may inherit —rnal life? *Mark 10:17*

21. Mine hour is not — come. *St. John 2:4*

23. The — number of them is to be redeemed. *Num. 3:48*

25. — it, even to the foundation thereof. *Ps. 137:7*

26. The Garden of —

27. He is risen from the —. *Matt. 27:64*

28. — not: for, behold, I bring you good tidings of great joy. *Luke 2:10*

29. It is a — thing that the king requireth. *Dan. 2:11*

30. He shall rule them with a rod of —. *Rev. 2:27*

31. He was — at that ... and went away grieved. *Mark 10:22*

35. The — Testament

38. Your — shall be turned into joy. *St. John 16:20*

39. The poor man had ... one little — lamb. *II Sam. 12:3*

41. The Lord is my strength and my —. *Ps. 28:7*

42. —fess your faults one to another. *James 5:16*

44. He calleth them all by their —. *Ps. 147:4*

47. The — found no rest for the sole of her foot. *Gen. 8:9*

49. — that man, and have no company with him. *II Thess. 3:14*

50. Thy — and thy she goats have not cast their young. *Gen. 31:38*

51. He took hold of his own clothes, and — them in two. *II Ki. 2:12*

52. My God, why —t thou forsaken me? *Mark 15:34*

53. With God — things are possible. *Mark 10:27*

54. There came w— men from the east. *Matt. 2:1*

56. With silver, iron, —, and lead, they traded. *Ezek. 27:12*

This Diagramless is 15 boxes wide by 15 boxes deep.

ACROSS

1. Aries constellation
4. That woman
7. Consumed
8. Five pairs
9. Word with "snow" and "thunder"
11. School-test mark
13. Sombrero
15. Podded vegetable
16. Dull routine
17. Newspaper: slang
20. Woe is me!
22. Lovers' quarrel, e.g.
24. Window glass
25. — out, distribute
26. Reside temporarily
27. Squander
28. Christian festival
30. Penalty
31. For each
32. That man's
33. Appear to be
35. Distract
38. Excalibur, e.g.
40. Uncouth
41. Perennial flower
44. Folk knowledge
45. Come upon
46. Change of —, variation
47. Still
48. Wrestler's pad
49. Blunder
52. Moisture droplets
53. Fur scarf
55. Slipknot loop
57. Classifieds
58. Commotion
59. Golf peg
60. Lair

DOWN

1. Stool pigeon: slang
2. Upon
3. Simple
4. Swagger
5. Police: slang
6. Terminate
9. Declare
10. Become proficient at
11. Confederate color
12. Expunge
13. Amateur radio operator
14. Pub brew
18. Picnic pest
19. Gosh!
21. Mediterranean or Caspian
23. Average
24. Review (a play) unfavorably
26. Wineglass part
27. "Fresh": slang
29. Raced
30. V, today
32. Concealed
33. Out of —, cross
34. Before: poetic
35. Dull grayish-brown
36. Actor Taylor
37. Exchange
38. Cunning
39. Great grief
40. Ritual
42. Diamonds: slang
43. Stitch
45. Bogus
48. Method or form
50. Route
51. Was conveyed in
54. Make lace
56. Daughter's brother

This Diagramless is 15 boxes wide by 15 boxes deep.
Starting box is on the last page.

ACROSS

1. Strike lightly

4. Is concerned

6. Make a remark

8. Drill (a hole)

9. "Sailing to Byzantium," for one

11. Took delight in

12. Sugary

14. Yearn (for)

15. Fourth planet from the sun

17. More rational

18. Smacks

20. Quiche ingredient

21. Storied item under a mattress

22. Sunday-to-Saturday periods

25. Expected wishfully

27. Plumbing complaint

28. Had a debt

29. Bus-route halting places

32. Upbraid

34. Cleveland's lake

35. Racing circuits

36. Bank employees

38. Missteps on ice

39. Adjust, as a clock

DOWN

1. Domesticated

2. Sleeve insert

3. Nest sounds

4. Apple or pear part

5. Word with "man" or "mobile"

6. Take —, seek shelter

7. Abounds

8. — up, cram

10. Restaurant purchase

11. Continues to stay

13. Ensnared

14. Summoned publicly

16. Racer's need

17. Emulate a seamstress

19. Lugubrious

23. Flying toy

24. Golf or tennis

25. Basketball targets

26. Hooting avians

30. Crusted desserts

31. Auctions off

32. Snoozed

33. Elevator cages

37. Falsehood

125

ACROSS

1. Juliet's weapon
7. Droops suddenly
13. Star: French
14. Tokyo's island
15. Tagger
16. Region of Northern Europe
18. Switch setting
19. Thus: Latin
21. Din
22. Also
23. British street-car
25. Tennis-match division
26. State positively
27. Harsh
29. Fleet of ships
31. Mouths: Latin
32. Curved line
33. Freight-carrying boats
36. "Swipes"
39. Noble family of early Italy
40. Soak
42. Revise, as a manuscript
43. Donkey
44. Certain soft drinks
46. Single unit
47. Therefore
48. Advent
50. AMA member: abbr.
51. Camera stand
53. Scant dozen
55. "She — to Conquer"
56. Peaceful

DOWN

1. Believers in a god
2. Fine clothes
3. Green-light command
4. Baseball-great Hodges
5. Verve
6. Rest
7. California mountain
8. Solitary
9. German conjunction
10. Title for Steinem
11. Uses Bell's invention
12. Miscellaneous
17. Falsehood
20. Frolics
22. Alligator pear
24. Combine
26. Concur (with)
28. 1979 film, "Norma —"
30. Informer: slang
33. Brutes
34. Classify
35. Scimitars
36. Barrel parts
37. Basswood, for one
38. "Tristram Shandy" author
41. Actor Wallach
44. Harvest yield
45. Shopper's bonanza
48. Part of a military address: abbr.
49. The sea, in Irish myth
52. Greek maiden of myth
54. — Day, May 8th, 1945

HARD

154

ACROSS

1. Knight's title
4. Hysterical fear
9. Porky, for one
12. Miner's find
13. Unaccompanied
14. — carte: 2 wds.
15. Marred
17. Manicurist's concerns
19. Has creditors
20. Daze
21. Rescues
23. Kitchen surface
26. Vigoda and namesakes
27. Blouse
28. Behold!
29. — Angeles
30. Like many newspapers
31. Fill in (for)
32. Word with "portable" and "color": abbr.
33. Formal dances
34. Disappear gradually
35. Fastened
37. Treats for Fido
38. Inquires
39. Hinted
40. Squander
42. Corridor
45. Grow old
46. Hospital worker
48. Tennis stroke
49. Distress signal
50. Blemishes
51. Weep

DOWN

1. Turf
2. A Gershwin
3. Takes away
4. Book parts
5. Pub orders
6. Move the head in assent
7. At home
8. Ten decades
9. Brush on color
10. Ailing
11. Service station purchase
16. Influences by respect
18. Female relative
20. Dirties
21. Sprinkles with a seasoning
22. Over
23. Tot
24. Evade
25. Judges' garments
27. Auctions
30. Makes less bright
31. Summer shoes
33. Head-and-shoulders sculpture
34. Enemies
36. Crates
37. Public transports
39. Throw
40. Existed
41. Past
42. Tennis instructor
43. Moo — gai pan, Chinese menu item
44. Recede
47. Skyward

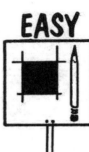
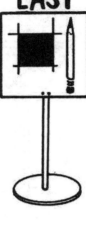

EASY

127

ACROSS

1. Overalls part
4. Baby's bed
8. Pirate's drink
12. "Diamonds — Forever"
13. Protagonist
14. Assistant
15. N.Y. baseball team
17. Fasten firmly
18. Lamprey
19. Talking bird: var. sp.
20. Sleepaway camper's luggage
23. Covered with wood sheets
26. Stag
27. Comic Foxx
28. — and behold!
29. Word with "age" and "cream"
30. Conjecture
32. State further
33. Compass point
34. Sensible
35. U.S. diving star Louganis
36. Imaginary troublemaker
38. SOS light
39. Daily fare
40. Mr. Costello
41. Cries noisily
43. Rascal
47. Garfield's friend
48. Emporium
49. Zodiac sign
50. Uniting force
51. "No ifs, —,or buts"
52. Composer of "The Star-Spangled Banner"

DOWN

1. Howl; bark
2. A Gershwin
3. Actor Vereen
4. Face part
5. Country dance
6. Tax agency: abbr.
7. Guitarist Diddley
8. Acquired
9. Compete with
10. Lyric poem
11. Understand
16. Superman's adopted surname
17. Lemon peelings
19. Ms. West and her namesakes
20. Inanimate object
21. Andretti's car
22. State of being: suffix
23. Primp
24. Forefather
25. Evade
30. Strong winds
31. Single thing
32. Former coach Parseghian
34. Grinned
35. Sullen
37. Newsman, — Newman
38. Stockades
40. Fat, e.g.
41. Choreographer Fosse
42. Fuss
43. Small closed truck
44. Kind; sort
45. Born
46. Play (with)
48. Graduate degree in the humanities: abbr.

ACROSS

1. Drink slowly
4. Walks back and forth
9. Lion or tiger
12. "We — the World"
13. Decorate
14. Street: abbr.
15. Gift-wrapper's need
17. In favor of
18. Mr. Rather
19. Stoplight color
21. Indefinite amount
23. Long steps
27. — fours, small dessert cakes
30. Press (clothes)
31. Artist's subject
33. Smallest State: abbr.
34. Mouse's kin
35. Removed the center of (an apple)
36. For each
37. Asner or Ames
38. Jury, for one
39. Sensible
40. VII, today
42. Tastes (a variety of foods)
44. "No ifs, —, or buts"
46. "— Are My Sunshine"
47. Take first prize
49. Building site
51. Inscribe
55. Highest card
56. Wear away
58. Cowboy Rogers
59. Affirmative!
60. Rose to one's feet
61. Ram's mate

DOWN

1. Tree fluid
2. A Gershwin
3. Energy
4. Peeled
5. Public notice
6. Policeman
7. "Goofs"
8. Pried
9. West Pointer
10. Ms. Gardner
11. Decade number
16. Ireland: poetic
20. Evil spirit
22. "Blazing Saddles" director Brooks
23. Fathers
24. Swap
25. Spoil
26. Blisters
28. Song, "Goodnight —"
29. Wearies
32. Postpone
35. Tapers, e.g.
36. Buddy
38. Writing tool
39. Urge
41. Wind-direction indicators
43. Cut (the lawn)
45. Kind; type
47. Method
48. Frozen water
50. Also
52. Wrath
53. Pull behind
54. Sight organ
57. Perform (an action)

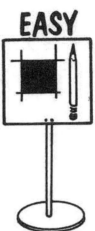

EASY

129

EASY

ACROSS

1. Vim; vigor
4. Hew
8. Tribe
12. "You — My Sunshine"
13. 60-minute interval
14. Solitary
15. Knight's title
16. Concerned with
17. Horses' goodies
18. TV's "— Street"
20. Mars, for one
22. Employ
23. Pointed summit
24. Bathing need
26. Classify
27. Gym pad
30. Do sums
31. Malice
32. Crude metal
33. Golly!
34. Nosegay
35. Adorable
36. First-rate: 2 wds.
37. Operate
38. Essences; cores
41. Bread spread
44. Land measure
45. Semiprecious stone
47. Dined
48. Slender
49. Ascend
50. Country hotel
51. Soft drink
52. Prophet
53. — "King" Cole, singer

DOWN

1. Go by
2. Great Lake
3. Convince
4. Ring out
5. Sharpen
6. Not in
7. Real estate
8. Capelike garment
9. Lend
10. Poker stake
11. Bird's home
19. Viper
21. Tardy
23. Composure
24. Droop
25. Lyric poem
26. Backers
27. Everest, for one
28. Masterly skill
29. Golf mound
31. Blot
35. Sever
36. Amphitheater
37. Straightedge
38. Head coverings
39. Reverberated sound
40. Desertlike
41. Foundation
42. Sicilian volcano
43. Lease
46. Bakery item

ACROSS

1. Allow
4. Upbraid; rebuke
9. Car for hire
12. "We — the World"
13. Indian boat
14. "Heart of Dixie": abbr.
15. Make ready
17. Silly mistake: slang
19. Museum display
20. Loving touch
21. Theater platform
24. Companions
25. Frilly fabric
26. Records on cassette
27. Perform
29. Presidential nickname
30. Prefers
31. Clear (of)
32. Myself
33. Goes by bus
34. Adore
35. Lawsuits
36. Secret languages
37. Divides
39. Burger holder
40. Wear away
41. Archery-range sights
45. — Vegas, Nev.
46. Lariat loop
48. Brief snooze
49. Soap ingredient
50. Footwear
51. Use a towel on

DOWN

1. Once around the track
2. Make a blunder
3. Golf peg
4. Frighten
5. Small wagon
6. Dollar bill
7. Behold!
8. Formal arguments
9. Walking sticks
10. Pub brews
11. "If you hum a few — . . ."
16. Part of a book
18. Metallic rocks
20. Sleeveless garments
21. Thin
22. Seize
23. One or eleven in many card games
24. Manufactures
26. Ocean movements
27. Plunge, as into water
28. Lyric poems
30. Pays attention
31. Fishing pole
33. Sudden attack
34. Of great duration
35. Nearby
36. Makes well
37. Vend
38. Beg; implore
39. Foundation
41. Also
42. Conclude
43. Street-paving substance
44. Intelligence agent
47. Cry of surprise

E A S Y

131 ABOUT-FACE CROSSWORD

HARD

by John Greenman

This special crossword is solved in the same way as a regular crossword, except that the words are written into the diagram either from right to left (for the BACKWARDS words) or from bottom to top (for the UP words). The answers to definitions 1-Across and 1-Up have been entered to help you get started.

BACKWARDS

1. Church service
5. Detection device
10. Lloyd Webber hit
14. Came to rest
15. Love: Italian
16. Feverishness
17. Prelates' tribunal
18. Metallic sounds
19. Ad man's euphemism for "low calorie"
20. Verbal woolgathering: 3 wds.
23. Smoothed
24. Pintail duck
25. Norse gods
28. Quick trip
32. Cultured item
35. Certain officeholders: abbr.
37. Canadian canals
38. Old oaths
39. Chemical suffix
40. Talent lookout
42. Cochlea location
43. Caviars
44. Deserves
45. Gladden

48. Fingerprint ridge
50. More's alternative
52. Ceramic workers
56. After reconsidering: 3 wds.
61. Deep ringing sound
62. French river
63. Ancient Dead Sea land
64. On the Banda
65. Diamond foul-up
66. Slave
67. Stag, e.g.
68. Bits of derring-do
69. Ragout

UP

1. Large stores
2. Hilo hello
3. Demonstration: hyph. wd.
4. Norm
5. White water
6. Ida — Dada
7. Bell sound
8. City of Greece
9. Job hunters' mailing
10. Phone user
11. Exchange fee

12. Ballet costume
13. Bird food
21. Bow-to-stern timbers
22. Patio: abbr.
26. Notion: comb. form
27. Begin again
29. Hebrew lyre
30. Part of speech
31. Specks
32. Chick's plaint
33. Equal: French
34. Swiss river
36. Dovetail
40. Prefix with "comic"

41. Bumps on the skin
43. Did a cobbler's job
46. Vinegar variety
47. Dry, as wine: French
49. Not us
51. Slumber sound
53. Pass off
54. North Sea feeder
55. Be a litterbug
56. O.T. book: abbr.
57. Facial feature
58. Large knife
59. Calamitous
60. Trampled

STORY CROSSWORD   EASY

by Eugene T. Maleska

Fill in the crossword diagram and the dashes, getting clues as you read along. When you have finished, you will have a complete story and a perfect puzzle. (-A means Across and -D means Down.)

WAITING GAME

I'll never forget the day I stopped for a bite at a dusty little (4-A)_____ just outside (6-A) _____ Angeles. This tall, skinny waiter prances over to my table and (9-A) _____ his hand under my cigar to catch the (20-A) _____ .

"Unless my (10-A) _____ deceive me," he says, "you're one of them talent scouts from Hollywood. Well, I can (1-D) _____ like a snake, hoot better than any pair of (16-D) _____ , (15-D) _____ like a toad and dance as good as (5-D)_____ Bolger. And I got a great singin' voice which don't need any (14-A) _____ chamber."

"Sorry," I replied. "I'm not a talent scout. And, now, if you please, I could (18-D) _____ a menu."

He ignored me. "(22-D) _____ , shucks! Just my luck! I gotta get out of this place. The work's too tough. I keep runnin' around here like a (7-A) _____ in a trap. You're the (8-D) _____ customer I've had in the last half-hour."

Impatiently, I glanced at my watch. "Waiter, I'm in a hurry. I have (2-D) _____ important (17-D) _____ to keep."

Again he brushed me aside. "You see the boss over there?" He pointed to a rotund woman behind the counter. "(23-A) _____ pays me a (3-D) _____ pittance. And to think that I come on (17-A) _____ every day at 8 A.M. on the (4-D) _____ ."

Angrily I rose and shook a finger (12-A) _____ his face. "Sir, I want to eat!"

"Okay, don't get so sore. Would you like a (1-A) _____ omelet?"

"(13-A) _____!"

"Well, (19-A) _____ about a (21-A) _____ of chop suey with (11-D) _____ sauce?"

I shook my head in disgust.

"Then, maybe some rhubarb (9-D) _____ ?"

"Absolutely not!"

He flicked his towel irritably. "That's the whole menu, fella! You've just had your (6-D) _____!"

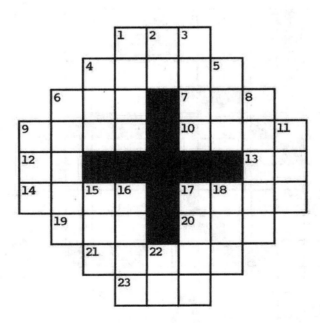

133

ACROSS

1. Get-up
5. Statutes
9. Observed
12. Culture medium
13. Medicinal plant
14. Spanish cheer
15. Fine porcelain pieces: 3 wds.
18. And not
19. Least good
20. Given to brooding
23. Smelting waste
25. Charles-family dog
26. Road: Latin
27. Corn unit
30. "The —," Lemmon/Fonda thriller: 2 wds.
33. Possesses
34. Gay song
35. Britain's Sir Anthony —
36. Part of AFB
37. Wishy-washy
38. Clean, in a way
41. Feather scarf
42. Trade ships: 2 wds.
48. Lout
49. Chief
50. Unimportant person
51. High explosive, for short
52. Social insects
53. U.S. singer/actor

DOWN

1. Chatter
2. Past
3. Had charge of
4. Playwright Behan
5. "Cowardly Lion" actor
6. Boxing great
7. Broke the tape
8. To open water
9. Acid-tasting
10. European peaks
11. Setting for " oaters "
16. Kittenish
17. Gear tooth
20. — number
21. Dept. of Labor agency: 2 wds.
22. Cornelia — Skinner
23. Fashion
24. Church season
26. Egyptian goddess
27. Musical passage
28. Portent
29. Bow
31. Yellowhammer State
32. Backward step
36. Chignon, e.g.
37. Jazz style
38. Aberdeen native
39. Biggers' detective
40. Fissure
41. Storage places
43. Preserve
44. Illuminated
45. Purpose
46. Free (of)
47. Watch secretly

ACROSS

1. Plains Indian tent
6. Seat
11. Wall paintings
12. Pitcher's adversary
14. Amino —
15. Screen from light
17. Thus
18. Employ
19. Rental contract
20. Flower beginning
21. Negative
22. Kind; type
23. Vaulting staff
24. One
25. Speed contest
26. Maxim used as a guiding principle
27. Surfer's need
28. Nonsense
29. Aromatic seasoning
31. Metal containers
32. Shortwave radio
34. Prong
35. Free-for-all
36. Concerning
37. Terminate
38. Remarkable thing: slang
39. Allow
40. — length, finally
41. The same
42. Protein source
43. Incentive
45. Italian's *venti*
47. Echolocation apparatus
48. Word with "common" or "horse"

DOWN

1. Arizona city
2. A Great Lake
3. Cushion
4. Overhead train
5. Fundamental nature
6. Pursuit
7. Conceal
8. Devoured
9. That thing
10. Consequence
11. Hawaiian volcano, — Loa
13. Where to see broncobusting
16. Second-place finisher in a fable
19. Depart
20. The two
22. Beauty of movement
23. Sheriff's band
26. Dollars, e.g.
27. Air in motion
28. Election tickets
29. Hot vapor
30. Spotted horses
31. Gael
32. Invent
33. Apple brown —
35. Bishop's headdress
38. Prima donna
39. Optical glass
41. Clamor
42. Human males
44. As far as
46. You and I

MEDIUM

135

HARD

ACROSS

1. Summit
4. Beaver product
7. Acclaim
12. I love: Latin
13. Past
14. Dan or Gad
15. Thayer's baseball poem: 4 wds.
18. River in England
19. Those people
20. River island
22. Fictional Plaza Hotel denizen
26. Play division
29. Israel's Golda
31. Sentence part
32. Longfellow work: 4 wds.
35. Listen to
36. Not too good: hyph. wd.
37. Total (up)
38. On a ship
40. Time period
42. Ms. Lupino and namesakes
44. Cosmetician Lauder
48. Longfellow poem (with "The"): 3 wds.
52. Jury, e.g.
53. Common conjunction
54. Mr. Onassis
55. — of, informed
56. Reply: abbr.
57. Put on

DOWN

1. Statesmanship
2. Poet Khayyám
3. Sit as a model
4. Office hours
5. Turkish title
6. Abolitionist, Lucretia —
7. Merman or Kennedy
8. Violin-making area
9. Monrovia is its capital: abbr.
10. Arab robe
11. Viet holiday
16. Alfonso's queen
17. Under —, secretly: 2 wds.
21. Communications satellite
23. Small amount
24. Irrational number
25. Geraint's mate
26. Baile — Cliath, Gaelic name of Dublin
27. Café employee
28. Greenish-blue color
30. Workers' group
33. Stove part
34. Woodlands
39. Bewilder
41. Mountain tree
43. Biblical country in Egypt
45. Amphibian
46. Prefix with mart or dollars
47. Ireland: poet.
48. IRS man: abbr.
49. Hem and —
50. Actress Claire
51. Convent dweller

ACROSS

1. Mesh fabric
4. Was concerned
9. Feline
12. Ms. Gardner
13. Word with "branch" and "oil"
14. Mine product
15. British title
17. Solidify
18. Males
19. Convened
21. Mature, as fruit
23. Makes happy
27. Three-piece suit parts
30. Raise, as children
31. More modern
33. Surprised cry
34. Cereal grain
35. Step
36. Wonder
37. Added note: abbr.
38. Endures; stays
39. Luge, for one
40. Spirited horse
42. "Irish" and "English" dogs
44. Fishing poles
46. Born
47. Wedding words
49. Race unit
51. Certain shovel
55. Scarlet color
56. Big occasion
58. Put to rest
59. Ram's mate
60. Posts; mails
61. Fruit drink

DOWN

1. Capture
2. Ms. Gabor
3. Paving goo
4. Ice cream —, summer treats
5. Mr. Jolson
6. Assemble; fix
7. Always
8. Make (a speech)
9. Arrives
10. Have life; exist
11. Years in decade
16. Actor Sharif
20. Camp shelters
22. Miles — hour
23. Supports; holds up
24. Fewest
25. Dine; consume
26. Chairs
28. Tall edifice
29. Gets rid of
32. Become smarter
35. "English" and "Western" riding gear
36. Pub brew
38. Zodiac sign
39. Pace
41. Wear away
43. Exams
45. Conserve
47. Anger
48. Morning dampness
50. Writing tool
52. Pie — mode: 2 wds.
53. Mate for mom
54. Sight organ
57. Bismarck's State: abbr.

137

ACROSS

1. Expanded
5. Church bench
8. — school, private educational facility
12. Volcano output
13. Eon
14. Imitate a lion
15. Expert flyers
16. Negative word
17. Too
18. Bent, as a fender
20. Followed closely: slang
22. Pencil ends
24. Garden tool
27. Climbs
31. Assistance
32. Powerful explosive: abbr.
33. Affirmative vote
34. Interfered
37. Avid
39. Motives
41. Small horses
44. Flower features
48. Baking chamber
49. First woman
51. A Great Lake
52. Highest point
53. Competed in a marathon
54. Mature
55. Makes a mistake
56. Thoroughfares: abbr.
57. Impudent talk

DOWN

1. Happy
2. Speed contest
3. Level
4. Squandered
5. Ling-Ling, for one
6. Self
7. Dampest
8. Glorify
9. Bun
10. Alleviate
11. Urge
19. Before: poetic
21. Circle part
23. Smooths wood, in a way
24. Newsman Donaldson
25. Bakery item
26. Total (up)
28. Pester
29. Tint
30. Homily: abbr.
32. Puzzling problems
35. Consumes liquid
36. Civil War general
37. Compass point
38. Fall flowers
40. Unwraps
41. Pontiff
42. Finished
43. Close by
45. Diva's song
46. Facial features
47. Observes
50. Tub

ACROSS

1. Surrealist artist
5. Kind or sort
9. Dog's "hand"
12. Sign, as of a future event
13. Inheritor
14. Surface for Brian Boitano
15. Outlet
16. Introduce new methods
18. Goes into
20. Biblical garden
21. Squirrel food: plural
23. Be
26. Foolish
30. "... by the beautiful —"
31. Faithful
32. Consume
33. Meat and "veggie" dish
34. Intention
35. Starlike signs
37. James Dean film, "— Without A Cause"
39. Small stain
40. Requirement
42. Evaded, as a commitment
46. Assess too highly
49. Bread spread
50. That — then; this is now.
51. U.S. Government agents: hyph. wd.
52. In good health
53. Naval officer: abbr.
54. Mineral-spring resorts
55. Bird's home

DOWN

1. Symbol of peace
2. Prayer ending
3. Fasting period
4. Sharp; vivid
5. Scottish flowering plants
6. Hankering
7. Evergreen tree
8. Wears away
9. Borge and Cliburn
10. Perform, as in a play
11. Tiny
17. Irritate
19. Actress McClanahan
22. Chairs
24. Search for
25. Fancy marbles
26. Night "light"
27. Great Lake
28. Unfeeling state
29. Foster and King
33. Use a bench: 2 wds.
35. Warns
36. Caviar
38. Always: poetic
41. Moist
43. Merriment
44. Lampreys
45. Blockhead
46. Be in debt
47. Utility truck
48. Steeped beverage

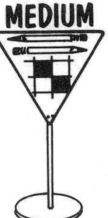

MEDIUM

139

EASY

ACROSS

1. Skilled
5. Foot covering
9. Social insect
12. Costly
13. Corn spikes
14. Dove's sound
15. Leaves
17. Concerns
19. Distress call
20. Desert beasts
21. Fragment
24. Measuring devices, for short
25. Leaping amphibian
26. Bestowed
27. Greeting
29. Lawn tree
30. Single item
31. Seed container
32. Cheyenne's State: abbr.
33. Talks
35. Grain-grinding place
36. Plant anchors
37. Convenient
38. Takes a photo
40. Jolt
41. Kitchen dipper
42. Drinking glass
46. Malt beverage
47. Rules of conduct
49. Molten rock
50. Ghost's word
51. Vending-machine opening
52. Paradise

DOWN

1. Calculate
2. Busy insect
3. Drink like a cat
4. Rubbed out
5. Matched collections
6. Possesses
7. Either
8. Elude
9. Measures of land
10. Yuletide song
11. Throw
16. Actor Steiger
18. Prayer end
20. — in, collapses
21. Meat and veggie dish
22. Sacred
23. Crash (against)
24. Dyes
26. Sheeplike animals
27. Grasp
28. Lazily
31. Brooch
33. Calm
34. Lodging places
35. Sculpting material
36. Cowboy show
37. Incompetent actor: slang
38. Thick slice
39. Ring of light
40. Fair
42. A pair
43. Young boy
44. Resident of 52-Across
45. Moved swiftly
48. Actor Pacino

ACROSS

1. Farm sound
4. Trails
9. Small drink
12. Melody
13. Blacksmith's "workbench"
14. Sailor
15. Abundance
17. Japanese garment
19. Obtain
20. Evil spirit
21. Sprinkled
24. Fewer
27. Rooster's mate
28. Sharp knock
29. Varnish ingredient
30. Singer Jolson
31. Breathes
33. Compass point
34. Inclines
36. Tear
37. Mature
38. Concludes
39. More stable
41. Track events
43. Swinging door words
44. Restaurant worker
46. By word of mouth
49. Perform
50. Jazz stylist, Cleo —
52. Storm center
53. Affirmative reply
54. Haste
55. Matching collection

DOWN

1. Chart
2. Lubricate
3. Northwestern State
4. Dressmaker's guides
5. Some
6. Appliance store purchase: abbr.
7. Went on a scouting expedition
8. Slender
9. Pebbles
10. Author Fleming
11. Tennis instructor
16. Modern
18. Burrowing mammals
20. Leaves
21. Fine-grained rock
22. Singer Reddy
23. Stadium sound
25. Burn slightly
26. Scoff
29. Fixed
31. Insert
32. Recline
35. Confesses
37. Theater passageways
39. Leather thong
40. Genetic "building blocks": abbr.
42. "Electric" fish
44. Manner
45. Expert
46. Wallet item
47. Caustic substance
48. Still
51. That is (to say): abbr.

141

EASY

ACROSS

1. Stood for office
4. Snow vehicle
8. Dance movement
12. Marriage vow: 2 wds.
13. Angelic "head-dress"
14. Possess
15. Act
17. Out of bed
18. Biblical boat
19. Rhymester
20. Window hanging
23. Loftiest
26. Ripped
27. Inserted shoestrings
28. Informal greeting
29. Picnic pest
30. Lariats
31. Run (into) head-on
32. Boxing decision: slang
33. Rescued
34. Dwell
35. Reacted volcanically
37. Stormed
38. Bamboolike grass
39. Turf
40. Summoned
42. Remain: 2 wds.
46. On in years
47. Conduct
48. Put in service
49. Inquisitive
50. Boat paddles
51. Sunbather's goal

DOWN

1. Tear (apart)
2. Fruit drink
3. Word with "neither"
4. Coast
5. Song bird
6. Shade tree
7. Perform
8. Protect
9. Sample, as food
10. Night before
11. Animal enclosure
16. Lose coloring
17. Acting parts
19. Walked nervously
20. Tent peg
21. Pay homage to
22. Museum display
23. Recorded on "ribbon"
24. Remove a beard
25. Clocked, as a race
27. Was wild about
30. Had status
31. Trailer truck
33. Fast
34. Gent's companion
36. Encourages
37. Highways
39. TV headliner
40. Dip for gold
41. Long —, time past
42. Body of water
43. Deposit
44. Canada's neighbor: abbr.
45. Decimal base
47. Behold!

ACROSS

1. Resin
6. Boundary
11. Spicy sausage
12. Battery terminals
14. Greedy
15. Distress call
17. Defeat
18. Cruise port
19. Disconcert
21. Arab robe
22. Pronoun
23. Love or fear
25. Thus
26. Wooded
28. Adequate
30. Devour
31. W.W. II group: abbr.
32. Paul Hogan character, Mick —
35. Builds
38. Not: prefix
39. Cheated
41. By
42. Purpose
44. River in Germany
45. Expire
46. Biblical man
48. Poem
49. Sewing machine inventor
50. Guarantee
52. Helix
54. Horse
55. Giant

DOWN

1. Hole
2. Medley
3. Cushion
4. Common verb
5. European capital
6. Movie/TV animal
7. Amidst
8. Rabble
9. Notion
10. "Cuppa" requirement: 2 wds.
11. Hindu garments
13. Cache of money: slang
16. Cereal morsel
19. Non-professional
20. Recipient of special recognition
23. Get around
24. Nuzzled
27. Man's nickname
29. Home of the Trojans: abbr.
32. Man's name
33. Labor groups
34. Reiterated
35. Hemingway
36. Chinese island
37. Tough alloy
40. Concealed
43. Spar
45. Woman's name
47. Tint
49. Strike
51. Scale tone
53. Greek letter

This Diagramless is 17 boxes wide by 17 boxes deep.

ACROSS

1. Taxi
4. Cave dweller
7. First man
9. Window glass
10. Like a queen
12. Sticky "stuff"
13. Kings' homes
15. "Merry" month
18. Old horse
21. Challenge
22. Yarn
23. Conceit
24. Use a chair
25. Mental faculties
26. Animal doctor, for short
27. Molars
30. Smallest bill
31. Guided
32. Fuel for 1-Down
33. Free (from)
35. Mistake
37. "Man's best friend"
38. Shy
40. Transgression
41. Pea holder
42. Drink like a cat
43. Vigor
45. Oyster gem

47. Water barrier
48. Penalty
49. Obese
50. Expert
51. Abode of 7-Across
52. Remain
54. Sleeping place
55. Marry
56. Went to bed
59. Olympics plunges
60. Measuring stick
64. Article
65. Dreadful
66. Animal enclosure
67. Cushion

DOWN

1. Gas guzzler
2. Fruit drink
3. Sack
4. Bottom
5. Picnic pests
6. It follows "ess"
8. Road chart
9. Step
11. Women
12. Average
14. Tardy
15. Orono's State
16. Changes

17. Affirmative
18. At no time
19. Got older
20. Obtained
22. A pair
24. For 44-Down only
28. Stumble
29. That man
31. Solitary
32. Supreme Being
34. Split
36. Tear
37. Dunce
38. Domesticated
39. Ate in style
41. Humble request
42. Tatted product
44. Males
46. From a distance
47. Touch lightly
48. Not many
52. Stalk
53. "My County — of Thee"
56. Ceremony
57. Equal
58. Failure: slang
59. Short swim
61. Mouth part
62. Historic period
63. "Angry" color

144

EASY

ACROSS

1. Not well
4. Leather fastener
9. Baby's perch
12. Oolong or Pekoe
13. Taunt
14. Lyric poem
15. "Sweet" age
17. Black bird
19. Dress edge
20. Lateral edge
21. Location
24. Under high water
27. Khomeini's land
28. Forays
29. Behold!
30. Allow
31. Heavy twines
32. Newscaster Brokaw
33. Scale note
34. Picture holder
35. Cassette
36. Rivers
38. Fathers
39. Auto pioneer
40. Cot, for one
41. Stable unit
43. Fred Flintstone, for one: 2 wds.
47. "For — a jolly good . . ."
48. Wipe out
50. Be in debt
51. So far
52. Police warning
53. Home animal

DOWN

1. That thing's
2. Flower garland
3. Not strict
4. Spirited horse
5. Rain hard
6. Raced
7. While
8. Punctuation marks
9. Adored
10. Summer quaff
11. Writing tool
16. Comparison word
18. Fusses
20. Playground sight
21. Window parts
22. Goody
23. Consume
24. Cultivates
25. Wed secretly
26. Cupolas
28. Wanders
31. Rocking beds
32. Paving material
34. Dropped down
35. Neap or ebb
37. Meat cut
38. "Lucky" number
40. Foundation
41. Timid
42. Golf peg
43. Automobile
44. Swab
45. Wonder
46. Tennis need
49. Ocean State: abbr.

ANAGRAM CROSSWORD

MEDIUM

Every word in this puzzle is an anagram of the "word" given in the "definition"—that is, you will have to rearrange the letters of each "definition" to find the word to be entered into the diagram.

ACROSS

1. Prate
6. Tho
9. Pea
12. Vaboe
13. Era
14. Ads
15. Teems
16. Ewe
17. Sip
18. Snick
20. Stew
21. Car
24. On
25. Means
26. Mood
28. Curer
31. Gede
32. Are
33. Seve
37. Drier
39. Lose
40. Stain
43. Me
45. Tiw
46. Tail
47. Alert
50. Nit
51. Bat
52. Lager
56. Cae
57. Eon
58. Canoe
59. Den
60. Dew
61. Stens

DOWN

1. Mat
2. Bea
3. Top
4. Neve
5. Siren
6. Kawh
7. Sore
8. Ete
9. Panes
10. Apses
11. Diets
19. Coder
20. Swear
21. Dae
22. Dor
23. Goc
25. Um
27. Remit
29. Eer
30. Trace
34. Wov
35. Lie
36. Est
38. Ni
40. Stana
41. Lacie
42. Dinet
44. Lemon
47. Elan
48. Bead
49. Care
51. Two
53. Ers
54. Tag
55. Sen

146

MEDIUM

ACROSS

1. Short sleep
4. Parade display
9. Poultry product
12. Cain's mother
13. Rent
14. By way of
15. Armed conflict
16. Industrious insect
17. Kingdom
19. Rapid
21. Baby's bed
22. Newly-made
24. Taunt
25. Be without
26. Make a response
27. Perform
29. Actor Carney
30. Perceive
31. Edible pod
32. "Ain't — Got Fun"
33. Pursue
34. Be needful
35. Window covering
36. Humor
37. Self-conceit
39. Color lightly
40. Build
41. Negligent
42. Small bite
45. Observe
46. Marry in secret
48. Historic period
49. Paving substance
50. Assessed
51. Scarlet

DOWN

1. Recent
2. Actress Gardner
3. Flawless
4. Glint
5. Fasting season
6. Cereal grain
7. TV soap, "— the World Turns"
8. Patio
9. Elude
10. Fish breathing apparatus
11. Baseball or football
18. Orient
20. Inquire
21. Stop
22. Defect
23. Unusual
24. Anxious
26. Prepared
27. Fender mishap
28. Solemn vow
30. Break into pieces
31. Spouse
33. Stylish
34. Be victorious
35. Smile of scorn
36. Jumbled
37. Part of a three-piece suit
38. Region
39. Word with "measure" and "recorder"
41. Land parcel
43. Wrath
44. Cushion
47. Musical scale tone

ACROSS

1. Animal's den
5. Maui garland
8. Fifty percent
12. Light tan
13. Sea eagle
14. Exchange fee
15. Banner
17. Peace symbol
18. Bribe
19. Reflections
21. Arcane slang
24. Identifying mark
25. Hindu teacher
26. Cooking utensils
30. Mine entrance
31. Oscar Wilde, for one
32. Title
33. Refresh; revive
35. Party to: 2 wds.
36. Dossier
37. Bergen dummy
38. Human being
41. Gullet
42. Jai —
43. Demosthenes specialties
48. Slender
49. Pallid
50. Asian language
51. Orson Welles role
52. Usual Le Carré hero
53. School dances

DOWN

1. Guitarist Paul
2. Take steps
3. Elder Gershwin
4. Is stopped by the clock: 4 wds.
5. Spring
6. Go astray
7. Signify
8. Engaged someone in quarreling: 5 wds.
9. All excited
10. Reside
11. Enemies
16. Period
20. Gym pad
21. Culture medium
22. Impolite
23. Toothy smile
24. Venomous ill will
26. Capistrano birds
27. Narrow way
28. Love: Spanish
29. Transmit
34. By way of
37. Perched
38. Dissemble
39. Cooking pot
40. Maugham play
41. Goodly number
44. Talk: slang
45. Triumphant cry
46. Forty winks
47. Family member, for short

HARD

In this puzzle you can discover the caption for the cartoon below. Solve the crossword just as you would a regular puzzle. All of the words in the caption are to be found in the squares which have been circled in the puzzle. Now take the encircled words and arrange them into a suitable caption for the cartoon.

CAPTION:_____

ACROSS

1. Fight; quarrel
6. Pack too full
10. Shrub
14. Angry
15. Travel by bus
16. Burma's continent
17. Subway fare
18. Aid, as in wrongdoing
19. Firearms
20. Lamb's mother
21. Is able to
23. Garfield, to Jon
25. Play division
26. Expensive fur
27. Streetcar
29. Backless seat
32. "Me and — Shadow"
33. Without feeling
34. Border
38. "The loneliest number"
39. Cold and damp
40. Become less intense
42. Irene Cara hit
43. Depart
45. Shrink, as from fear
46. Thailand, for one
51. Portal
53. Fruit drink
54. Night before Christmas
55. For what reason?
56. Abraham's nephew
59. Loud ringing, as of bells
61. Otherwise
63. Oily fruit
65. Peel
66. Authentic
67. Seized
68. Besides
69. Swiss hero, William —
70. Put forth energetically

DOWN

1. Location
2. Jackdaw
3. Garden tool
4. Had lunch
5. Writing implement
6. Irritable person
7. Tease: slang
8. Highly skilled
9. Unit of length
10. Sack
11. Customary
12. From then until now
13. Quick
22. "— apple a day . . ."
24. Actor Selleck
26. Capone's gang: slang
28. Soap ingredient
29. Winter flakes
30. Sandwich fish
31. Portent
35. Make a sketch
36. Chess, for one
37. Water pitcher
41. Hen product
42. In favor of
44. Lyric poem
45. Prairie wolf
46. Greek "K"
47. Perfect model
48. Approaches
49. Open, as an act
50. Confused fight
51. Reside
52. Cry of wonder
56. Enjoy
57. Above
58. Circus structure
60. Zodiac sign
62. Actor Mineo
64. Careless

181

149

E A S Y

ACROSS

1. Beaver's handi-work
4. Thick piece
8. Banner
12. Hockey surface
13. Small horse
14. Perform again
15. Mealtime treat
17. Changed addresses
18. Gritty soil
19. Departed
20. Slope
22. Object to
25. Carry on, as a campaign
26. Category
27. "— way!," never
28. Had lunch
29. Physical form
30. Feline
31. Myself
32. Blackboard material
33. Concern
34. Pledge
36. Actors' parts
37. Ready to use
38. Like a sky-scraper
39. Iridescent stones
41. Land an air-craft: 2 wds.
44. Social engage-ment
45. Narrow road
46. Enemy
47. Coloring agents
48. Metal sources
49. Not many

DOWN

1. Performed
2. Expert
3. Main idea
4. Disbursed (money)
5. British noble-man
6. Crawling bug
7. Beside
8. Outward appearances
9. River embank-ment
10. Fruity drink
11. Deity
16. Rational
17. Deer's kin
19. Vine fruit
20. Marsh
21. After some time
22. Shallow dish
23. Animal trap
24. Hauls
26. Funnyman, Chevy —
29. Slides
30. Cancel, as a game: 2 wds.
32. Grins
33. Unfriendly
35. Speak pom-pously
36. Prices
38. Melody
39. Out of the ordinary
40. Word with "check" and "day"
41. Equal status
42. Misery
43. Recent
45. — and behold!

ACROSS

1. Presidential nickname
4. Digging tool
9. Wily
12. Family member
13. Hair dressing
14. "Annabel Lee" poet
15. Netherlands
17. Shallot
19. Well-ventilated
20. "Noshes"
21. Bottle stoppers
23. Cooking unit
24. Push (on)
25. Spacious
26. Business title: abbr.
28. "Norma — ", Sally Field role
29. Weather word
30. Sticky stuff: slang
31. Raised railroad
32. Book's name
33. Envelop
34. Monetary penalties
35. Bucket handles
36. Holds fast (to)
38. Destroy
39. Rustic
40. Co-worker
43. Pacino and Hirt
44. Choose
46. Historic period
47. Excepting
48. Musical sounds
49. Desert-like

DOWN

1. Hardwood tree
2. Scary word
3. Increase in size
4. Heavenly twinklers
5. Small horse
6. Furthermore
7. Princess of Wales, informally
8. Government concern
9. Cinnamon, for one
10. See
11. Longings
16. Admire
18. Sea force
20. Marble or granite
21. Remedy
22. Not written
23. Stains
25. Is important
26. Hockey score
27. Swabs
29. Curl
30. Smiled
32. Singer Turner
33. "Cool one's heels"
34. Primary
35. Lancaster and Reynolds
36. Seafood choice
37. "Humdinger": slang
38. Competition
40. Animal enclosure
41. Make a mistake
42. Singer-pianist Charles
45. Behold!

151

EASY

ACROSS

1. Occupied a chair
4. Cole slaw, for one
9. Wet earth
12. Single item
13. Exchange; swap
14. Mine product
15. Guided, as a boat
17. Theater platform
19. By way of
20. Inclined
21. Spring flower
24. Twists out of shape
25. Milky stone
26. Desires
27. Santa's syllable
29. Use oars
30. Annoy
31. Taxi
32. 14th letter
33. Cent
35. Dull person
36. Clock pointers
37. Showy flower
38. Pushes
40. Cooking vessel
41. External
42. Maybe
46. Pub beverage
47. Hail; welcome
49. Fib
50. Buddy
51. "The Best — of Our Lives," 1946 movie
52. Church bench

DOWN

1. Distress signal
2. Picnic pest
3. Golfer's peg
4. Comic —, newspaper feature
5. Region
6. Youth
7. TV commercial
8. Camel's domain
9. Complainer's sounds
10. Drive onward; impel
11. Feat of skill
16. Wicked
18. Nighttime bugle-call
20. Tall and lean
21. Ripped
22. "Once — a time . . ."
23. "L.A. —," TV show
24. Cautions
26. Breezes
27. Heavenly instrument
28. Follow orders
31. Policeman: slang
33. Surface (a road)
34. Solar —, sun power
35. The two
36. Traveler's lodging
37. Harbors
38. Cleaning substance
39. Hawaiian dance
40. Look closely
42. Pod dweller
43. High mountain
44. Pizza unit
45. Stitch
48. "Do, —, mi . . ."

ACROSS

1. River into the Colorado
5. Triumphant exclamation
8. State further
11. Part of Q.E.D.: Latin
12. Louis XIV, for one: French
13. Become hazy
14. Catch
15. TV barrister and wife
17. Flees from
19. Agency in charge of US buildings: abbr.
20. Political cartoonist
21. Rose essence
24. Bus-trip layover: 2 wds.
28. Nordic capital
29. Proceedings: Latin
30. Compass point
31. Penury
32. Iran ruler, once
33. Auto contest: 2 wds.
35. Greek goddesses of seasons
37. Listener's response: 2 wds.
38. "Tea for —"
39. American short-story writer

43. Snipers
46. Except for
47. Ancient Roman calendar date
48. Creative skill
49. Kiln
50. Sturdy tree
51. Sibilant
52. Foreign: comb. form

DOWN

1. Heredity factor
2. Tax shelters, once
3. Secular
4. They play at the Omni: 2 wds.
5. Lightning —
6. They play at the Astrodome: 2 wds.
7. Purpose
8. Completely bewildered: 3 wds.
9. Proper
10. Greek money: abbr.
13. They play at Fenway Park: 3 wds.
16. What Nicklaus and Palmer belong to: abbr.
18. Ballet step

22. Actor Guinness
23. Poked fun at
24. Imprudent
25. Parrot
26. Futuristic TV show: 2 wds.
27. Farm laborers
34. German article
36. Dawn goddess
40. Church section
41. Smooth out
42. Nevada city
43. "O Sole —"
44. Oklahoma city
45. Miss West

HARD

FIT-IN CROSSWORD

MEDIUM

To solve this crossword, place all the words in the Word List into the diagram, Kriss-Kross style. The words are listed in alphabetical order according to the number of letters in each word; the Across words and the Down words are mixed together. Each word will be used once and only once, so it's a good idea to cross off each word as you use it. We have entered one word to help you get started.

2 LETTERS
Ad
Am
Ed
Ra

3 LETTERS
Abe
Ade
And
Ape
Ava
Ave

Cod
Eat
Ewe
Eye
Had
Ira
Pay
Pin
She
Shy
Sol
Sty
Ten

Tin
Tip
Use
Van

4 LETTERS
Abet
Aver
Dear
Dire
Eden
Edge
Edna

Erin
Ever
Grow
Have
Hide
Mere
Rent
Ride
Rise
Saar
Save
Sham
Shun
Star
Stew
Tape
Tide
Tidy
Tone
Weed
Yale

5 LETTERS
Adore
Event
Never
Range
Satyr
Shape
Siren
Upend
Viper

6 LETTERS
Energy
Mentor
Second
Senate

8 LETTERS
One-sided
Returned

WHICH WORD CROSSWORD

MEDIUM

For each space Across and Down, one of the three words given is the word which will correctly complete the puzzle. It's up to you to figure out which word in each trio is the correct one. There is only one correct solution, and no word appears more than once in the completed puzzle.

ACROSS

1. Ran, raw, lop
4. Dover, naval, lines
6. Tetanus, heroine, liberal
8. Valor, chord, cover
9. Pen, I.R.S., Mel
11. Singe, roves, sorts
12. Speed, vital, vinyl
14. Pacer, cones, caves
15. Cal, gas, god
16. Tip, sat, for
18. Urns, aged, ulna
19. Air, mob, mow
20. Tuna, Etta, stir
21. Nee, net, Nan
22. Cat, LPs, CPR
23. Prior, river, direr
24. Scour, seven, haven
26. Seams, salad, saber
27. Dad, try, yin
28. Lanes, lopes, motel
29. Animals, tamales, atrophy

31. Razed, evade, EPCOT
32. Yet, M.D.s, yes

DOWN

1. Roses, lobes, Lorne
2. Over, oval, avid
3. Nap, per, wan
4. Dives, liver, limbs
5. Lumps, snail, rapid

6. Tends, loved, Herod
7. Lon, let, etc.
8. Vacancy, connect, coveted
10. Lefties, natural, sisters
11. Soles, Sarah, rages
12. Vow, lob, err
13. Laura, lined, dries
14. Can, pan, pun
15. Gap, car, got
17. Par, pro, ram

19. Apt, man, m.p.h.
20. Tiles, empty, siren
22. Crane, *lente*, cedar
23. Panic, dated, ripen
25. Ira, vat, via
26. Soles, sleep, sonic
28. Lace, load, maze
30. Ivy, may, r.p.m.

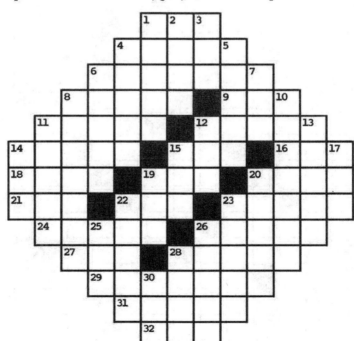

155

E A S Y

ACROSS

1. Bottle top
4. Provide food
9. Fold-up bed
12. Lyric poem
13. Idolize
14. Wonder
15. Giver
17. Comic Conway
18. Sandra or Ruby
19. Marry
21. Short letter
23. Slim
27. What a candidate wants
30. A very large amount
31. Given to prying: var. sp.
33. Richmond's State: abbr.
34. Fishing pole
35. Ceases
36. Operated
37. While
38. Glue's kin
39. Walk in water
40. Tasty pie nut
42. A Woody Allen comedy
44. Actor, Alan —
46. Race unit
47. Thick mist
49. Dixie State: abbr.
51. Dazes
55. Anger
56. Window sill
58. Ocean
59. Four-poster, for one
60. Oozes
61. Slippery fish

DOWN

1. Food fish
2. Fuss
3. Writer's tool
4. Showed concern
5. Paid notice
6. Small child
7. Ireland: poetic
8. Takes away
9. West Point student
10. Be in debt
11. Golf peg
16. Has
20. Fender benders
22. Plaything
23. Leather band
24. Not tight
25. Finish
26. Plant parts
28. Avoid
29. More rational
32. Brief time
35. Summery shoes
36. Knock sharply
38. Buddy
39. Cried
41. Confined, as a bird
43. Relieves
45. Towards shelter
47. Small lie
48. Mine deposit
50. Fruit drink
52. Utilize
53. Wedding announcement word
54. "My Gal —"
57. Family doctor: abbr.

M E D I U M

ACROSS

1. Housekeeper
5. Ma's mates
8. Gun discharge
12. Car part
13. Illuminated
14. Pueblo tribe member
15. Abound
16. Southern State: abbr.
17. "Abbey —," Beatles album
18. Examines ore
20. Tease; heckle
22. Snood
23. Tooth specialist's degree: abbr.
24. Obstacles
28. Colorado ski resort
32. Western country: abbr.
33. Primp
35. — Jima
36. "Uptight"
38. Stupors
40. Skill
42. Supped
43. Counsel
46. Admirals
50. Banister
51. "You — My Lucky Star"
53. Anger
54. Italian river
55. Lancelot's title
56. Otherwise
57. Beverage made from malt barley
58. Newspaper bigwigs: abbr.
59. Peruse

DOWN

1. — Hari
2. Hatchets
3. Capri and Manx: French
4. Order
5. Wall imperfection fixer
6. Have the flu
7. Remain upright
8. Tatters
9. Criminal, for short: slang
10. Milky gem
11. Ocean movement
19. Puppies at night, often
21. Radiate
24. Jungle abode
25. Custom
26. Jogged
27. Become colorfast
29. Photo: slang
30. Woolly mama
31. Ten, twenty, thirty, etc.: abbr.
34. Pencil ends
37. Popeye, is one
39. Closer
41. Taunt
43. Desert nomad
44. Challenge
45. "Hall of Ivy" cover
47. It's "as good as a miss"
48. Lioness of film
49. Require
52. Free (of)

PUNANAGRAMS HARD

by Mel Taub

Punanagrams are tricky but fun to solve. Definitions may be jokes or puns on the word wanted, or an anagram of the word itself. Generally there's a straight definition as a clue, too. For example, the answer to 5-Down is LINE. *Neil* is the anagram, with "Short note" as an additional clue. Roman numerals may be used; the words YOU, ARE, EYE, SEE, etc., might stand for U, R, I and C, respectively; "energy" could stand for the letters N, R, G, or "any" for N E. Consider the definitions from all angles and you will find they do make definite sense. And, have fun!

ACROSS

1. Lois, Sam and fellow countrymen
8. Leah's source of oil
13. It will flow duly if it has this property
14. Who child may entrap
16. Ship's crew? It learns the ropes
17. This Indian has no idea
18. Fashionable spouse is a convict
19. They sailed with Austrians in USA departure
21. Kind of dry
22. Note return to school
23. Anna's follower?
24. Dropping case of rum cakes in darkness
25. One of a thousand leaving armed
26. Raises cane, like Sam: Fr.
28. See what's in veins
29. Name in the New Deal. No?
31. Best articles for moderates?
33. A very small part of a cat?
34. Having reason or not
35. Inaner opera
37. They feel th' loss of urgency
40. Perfect words for shuffler
41. Steps of fashion, so to speak
43. Ira is behind this tree

45. Actor who did not care for manicure
46. Contemptible name
47. Hack follower?
48. Do for a penny, in short
49. Bird who sang the same two notes
50. Soprano sporting berets
52. Author who uses the post office?
54. Close friend? It ain't me!
56. Materials used on LST. See?
57. Where Alan sees ships
58. Man or eagle, i.e.
59. Feminist Lucretia was first to be spotted

DOWN

1. Distorted Dante: Sl.
2. What you do to me? You make me obsolete
3. One of 50 main Italian cities
4. Where miners go in at 500-1
5. Short note to Neil
6. End of term
7. Method for making messy tea
8. 'Taint starboard
9. Herr Nash
10. Carew's middle name

11. Rules, i.e., of relaxation
12. Continues until the end? Sure!
13. Sounds like monk is a little chicken
15. Word of gratitude in Brooklyn?
20. He did one fool after another in
23. To prod me is what was suggested beforehand
24. Go to Met to hear this
26. The overweight Mr. Capone and what crossing him could be
27. A negative prefix
28. Once a means of water travel
30. Miss Turner & I on veranda
32. A 50 lb. attachment to chain
35. Give Ted a cue
36. Terrine for annuitant Parisian

38. Can henna be derived from this herb?
39. Word weatherman deletes in summer
40. 2,000 is a number who follow the leaders
42. Philosophy native to Siam and China
44. Cash additions
46. Rome's inventor
47. Turk featured in "Lakme"
49. Store patronized by idle chef
50. Photo finisher
51. Might titlist sit out fight?
53. He stands amid silence
55. This one is a new beginner

158

E A S Y

ACROSS

1. Atlas feature
4. Brown, as bread
9. Apple centers
11. Distribute: 2 wds.
13. Make amends
14. Imitated
15. Negative vote
16. Call for help
17. Merchandise
19. Social insect
20. Oak or elm
22. "Danger" color
23. Escape
24. Parking areas
26. Cooks in water
27. Prepare for an exam
29. Injures
30. Window covering
31. Lease
32. Birthday-candle holder
33. Soap or chocolate unit
34. Secure
38. Mine find
39. Party —, souvenir
41. Deposit (an egg)
42. Elevator direction
43. Lawsuit
44. Similar
46. Narrates
48. Walked back and forth
49. Appraises
50. Marry

DOWN

1. Engine
2. Came up
3. Writing device
4. Recorded
5. Dollar bills
6. State further
7. "And — to bed . . ."
8. Underground passageways
9. Throw a fishing-line
10. Use needle and thread
11. Jack rabbits
12. Carries
18. Pretentious, in a way
19. Dismounted
21. Escape detection
23. Strongholds
25. "— to a Nightingale," poem
26. Hamburger roll
27. Keener
28. Capture; seize
29. Medal of Honor winner
30. Scrub clean
31. Talks wildly
33. Foundations
35. "Wonderland" visitor
36. Counterfeited
37. Observed
39. Destiny
40. Knock sharply
43. Mouse-catcher
45. Attorney's area
47. Creole State: abbr.

ACROSS

1. Rascal
6. Land of *flamenco*
11. Sudden rain
12. — to, act submissively
14. Word of choice
15. Strong feeling
17. TV's "One Life — Live"
18. Illuminated
20. One remaining
21. Edge
22. Burden
24. Hearing organ
25. Mickey and Minnie
26. Leave undone
28. Make broader
29. Roll of cloth
30. Tuneful combo
31. Sweeper
33. Large ape
36. Jump
37. Automobile
38. Nasty
39. Perform
40. Snooped
42. Heat source
43. Thus
44. Slim
46. Egyptian sun god
47. Experiment with: 2 wds.
49. Relish tray items
51. Thick
52. Award for valor

DOWN

1. Like The Alamo
2. Prefix meaning "joint"
3. Solemn wonder
4. Office note
5. Shield
6. Slopes "nut"
7. Needy
8. Grain beard
9. Tag game member
10. Observe
11. Lawmaker
13. Ladies
16. The one there
19. Harbor craft
21. Puzzling things
23. Single-masted vessel
25. Smallest amount
27. Shade tree
28. Armed conflict
30. Ennui
31. Trumpet sound
32. Written log
33. Profit
34. Hardy's partner
35. Magnani and Alberghetti
37. Greek island
40. In addition
41. Printer's word
44. Dad's boy
45. Free of
48. Biblical pronoun
50. Richmond's State: abbr.

159

MEDIUM

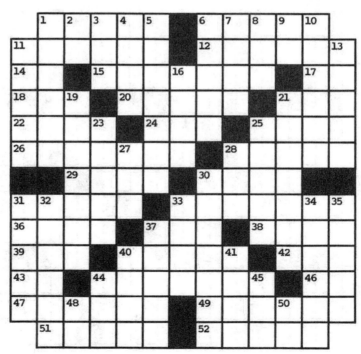

160

MEDIUM

ACROSS

1. Barbara — Geddes
4. Determinant
9. Cached away
12. In the past
13. Different
14. Mother sheep
15. British bastion: 3 wds.
18. Actor, Jack —
19. Turf
20. Eliot's "cruelest month"
22. Popeye's picker-upper
26. Circus insect
27. Nevada Lake
28. Greeting word
29. Wee fellow
30. Start upon
31. "Lamps of China" filler
32. Printer's dash
33. Jury, i.e.
34. Boring
35. Comes back
37. Appraises
38. Hill insect
39. Weed out
40. Famed prisoner in 15-Across: 2 wds.
46. Eisenhower, to pals
47. Wake up
48. Compete
49. Balloon filler, at times
50. Longhorn
51. Hearing organ

DOWN

1. Baseball need
2. Self
3. Let down
4. Yellowish pink
5. Tiny particle
6. Certain TV band: abbr.
7. Salt: French
8. Shore problem
9. Hollywood's Hopper
10. — Jima
11. Lair
16. Mr. Kazan
17. Not any
20. In search of
21. B17 or DC3
22. Wise men
23. TV's Donahue
24. Andean land
25. Rome's seven
27. Opryland's State: abbr.
30. Trades
31. Survive
33. Flat-bottomed boat
34. Valley
36. Falsehoods
37. Sovereign
39. Lawyer's concern
40. Hairpiece
41. Alias preceder: abbr.
42. Decay
43. Regret
44. Actress Scala
45. Feminine pronoun

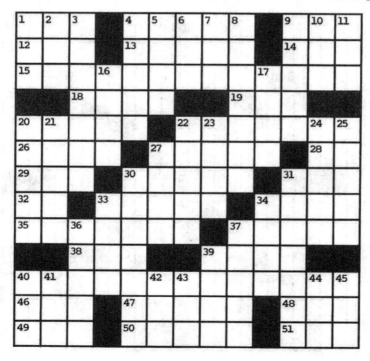

ACROSS

1. Mushroom top
4. Conform
9. Word with "shed" and "slip"
12. In the past
13. Dylan Thomas, e.g.
14. Former N.Y. mayor Beame
15. Contemporary of Titian
17. Singer John
19. Complain
20. Enticed
21. Narrow inlet
23. Intensely
24. Traditional knowledge
25. "Moola"
26. "You're — Vain"
28. Possess
29. Stingy soul
30. Voice: Latin
31. Mr. Kettle
32. Stored documents
33. Memphis' river
34. Relieve
35. Church's law
36. Oppose as false
38. Mud or slime
39. "Fantastic!"
40. Honorable
43. Indisposed
44. "Peer Gynt" creator
46. Make known
47. Understand
48. Onetime labor leader
49. Actor, Alejandro —

DOWN

1. Elevator cage
2. Moslem title
3. Snack at the Bijou
4. Judge's decision
5. Abstruse
6. Entirely
7. Pen pal's addition: abbr.
8. Presentation hall
9. Malicious
10. Hautboy
11. Travel: archaic
16. Rabbit cousin
18. *Fleur-de-lis*
20. Dice
21. Fail
22. Hawkeye State
23. Contrived
25. Italian metropolis
26. Like Lindbergh's flight
27. Beasts of burden
29. Wanderer
30. Salad topping
32. Fishing-net variety
33. Fascist
34. Eden's fruit
35. Like Kansas in August?
36. Osiris' wife
37. Donkey offspring
38. Unobstructed
40. Olympics initials
41. Hasten
42. Test
45. Exist

162

E A S Y

ACROSS

1. Derby or sombrero
4. Fall flower
9. That girl
12. Playing card
13. Protection from the sun
14. Crow's call
15. Depot
17. Damp and musty
19. Fruit drink
20. Looking glass
21. Form
24. The present
25. Much
26. Tea sweetener
27. Family member
29. "Honest — " Lincoln
30. Carries
31. Air cooler
32. In the direction of
33. Put off
34. Throw
35. Desert animal
36. Bottle stoppers
37. Post Office purchase
39. Dove's sound
40. Least favorable
41. Floor coverings
45. Skill
46. Run away and marry
48. Once around the track
49. Certainly!
50. Appointments
51. Cook in a skillet

DOWN

1. Owns
2. Perform
3. Steeped beverage
4. Out of the way
5. Slipper, for one
6. Beige
7. Mr. McMahon
8. Dwells
9. Frightening
10. Ring around the moon
11. Pitcher
16. Knocks lightly
18. Serving platter
20. Bills and coins
21. Venetian blind part
22. Tramp
23. Dined
24. Add up
26. Cavities
27. Halloween wear
28. Social insects
30. Enticed
31. Distant
33. Water barriers
34. Cage
35. Shoppers' vehicles
36. Apple centers
37. Swing
38. Ripped
39. Superman's garb
41. Folding bed
42. Dwarf
43. Paving substance
44. Secret agent
47. California city: abbr.

ACROSS

1. Track circuit
4. Relays
9. Past
12. Building addition
13. Driving maneuver: hyph. wd.
14. Author Fleming
15. Kramden portrayer
17. Weird
19. Alda or Hale
20. Black birds
21. Gotten up
23. Jabbed
24. High cards
25. Singer Reddy
26. Twelve inches: abbr.
28. Scarlet
29. Horseman
30. Ms. MacGraw
31. Actor Asner
32. King with the "Golden touch"
33. Hall-of-Famer Musial
34. Ideal
35. Actress Duke
36. Cutlasses
38. Cotton bundle
39. Jury
40. Wedding-ring holder: 2 wds.
43. Had a meal
44. Happening
46. In favor of
47. Pigpen
48. December figure
49. Actor Danson

DOWN

1. Drumstick
2. Everybody
3. Happy
4. Dey or St. James
5. Jacket style
6. Convent dweller
7. Physician: abbr.
8. Gym shoe
9. Ventilated
10. Profit
11. Single bills
16. Tavern orders
18. Level
20. Actor's resumé listings
21. Unusual
22. Frosted (a cake)
23. Bicycle part
25. Conceals
26. Like old soda
27. Small
29. Puzzling questions
30. Try
32. Greater amount
33. Seasoning
34. The "root of all evil"
35. Linguine, e.g.
36. Health resorts
37. Steam engine developer
38. Curved
40. Actor Vereen
41. Exist
42. Head movement
45. Monticello locale: abbr.

M E D I U M

QUIP CROSSWORD

MEDIUM

Look at words 1-Down, 31-Across, 7-Down, 14-Across, 37-Across, and 8-Down for the answer to the riddle:

What did Spiderman say to Little Orphan Annie?

ACROSS

1. Hit (a fly)
5. Small error
9. Business-letter abbr.
12. Ireland: Gaelic
13. Actress Turner
14. Fourth word of the quip
15. Went into
17. Louvre's city
19. Pull (a car)
20. Schoolday break
21. Scatter
24. Power
25. Sixty minutes
26. Brag
27. Doctor: abbr.
29. An — and a leg
30. Also
31. Second word of the quip
32. One of us
33. Hotel workers
35. Ernie's pal
36. Macaroni
37. Fifth word of the quip
38. Blouses
40. A long way
41. Verb form
42. Easter hats
46. "We — Family"
47. Fishing spool
49. Wicked
50. Indeed!
51. Storehouse
52. Say it isn't so

DOWN

1. First word of the quip
2. Finish first
3. Mr. Carney
4. Seesaw
5. Killed (a dragon)
6. Small boy
7. Third word of the quip
8. Last word of the quip
9. "— Grows in Brooklyn": 2 wds.
10. "— is Your Life"
11. Actress Harper
16. Use oars
18. Banking abbr.
20. Byways
21. Pillow cover
22. Ripped (open)
23. Pirate's drink
24. Actor, Henry —
26. Prepares (a hook) for fishing
27. AM: poetic
28. Obligation
31. Yearning
33. Fourth planet
34. Fall flowers
35. Overcooked
36. Xmas trees
37. Cooling device
38. Remain
39. In this place
40. Do origami
42. Hive dweller
43. First woman
44. Can metal
45. Like a fox
48. What?

EASY

ACROSS

1. Sheep's cry
4. Separately
9. Tennis teacher
12. Not well
13. Kind of beam
14. Boy
15. Bank clerks
17. Oscar or Emmy
19. Miner's find
20. Play parts
21. "Beauty's" boyfriend
24. In what place?
25. Shoe fastener
26. Selected
27. Peach State: abbr.
29. "— Maria," prayer
30. Atmosphere
31. Popular cookie-filler
32. Exist
33. Dried plum
35. Ocean breaker
36. Shut
37. Worn out; fatigued
38. Celebratory march
40. Came in first
41. Unaccompanied
42. Makes angry
46. "L.A. —," TV show
47. "Aida," for one
49. Not me
50. Finish
51. Actress Duncan
52. Ram's mate

DOWN

1. Chomped
2. Pub brew
3. Everyone
4. Watchful
5. Peel
6. Donkey
7. Note after do
8. Very small quantities
9. O'Hare transport
10. Uncommon
11. — and ends, scraps
16. Misplace
18. "The Way We —," film
20. Coast; beach
21. Gossip; chatter
22. Roof overhang
23. High card
24. Complaining sound
26. Make happen
27. Donate
28. Matured
31. Distant
33. Scheme
34. Cowboy's contests
35. Gust or gale
36. Mob; throng
37. Since this morning
38. Ashen
39. Actor Alda
40. Hospital division
42. Males
43. Potato bud
44. — or never
45. Take to court
48. Ma's partner

166

HARD

ACROSS

1. Among
5. Bird of prey
9. Law officer
12. Drill
13. Rival for Boris and Mats
14. Hail!
15. Mr. Dundee
17. Allow
18. Mister: Spanish
19. Very attentive: 2 wds.
21. Engrossed
23. Cap
24. "Sucker": slang
27. Binds
29. Location
32. Football number
34. Grumble
36. Voice range
37. Goad
39. Craving
40. Small seed
42. Ova
44. Country dance
47. Octave number
51. Mock
52. Fantasy: 2 wds.
54. Actress Ullman
55. Of an age
56. Author Gardner
57. Southern general
58. Auction off
59. Inert gas

DOWN

1. Rudiments
2. Further
3. Shackle
4. Interior scheme
5. Concealed
6. Fly
7. Divider
8. Showed reverence
9. — Jane
10. Past
11. Strokes
16. Use a soapbox
20. Compass point
22. Tailor's items
24. Barents, for one
25. Entire
26. Personal irritant: 2 wds.
28. Self-satisfied
30. Golfer's aid
31. Sea eagle
33. Vacuum
35. Enouraged
38. Foreign correspondent?: 2 wds.
41. Bishops of Rome
43. Charmer
44. Corridor
45. Ron Howard role
46. Telegram
48. "American Gigolo" actor
49. Angelic adornment
50. Government agents: hyph. wd.
53. Building addition

ACROSS

1. Auto fuel
4. Butt
7. Ames' location
11. So-so
13. Sound of a plucked string
15. Car's home
16. Catlike
17. Chill
18. Wheel projection
19. Cap
20. Drip
22. Smallest bit
23. Vigor
24. Entire amount
25. Chess pieces
26. Nobleman
28. You and I
29. Ax
31. Behold!
32. Mist
34. Have lunch
35. Small piece
36. Dress edge
37. Hole
38. Ponder
39. Sack
40. Cushion
41. Automobile
42. Imaginary
44. Mint output
47. Strict
48. Mailing expense
49. Remain
50. Matched pieces
51. Seed case

DOWN

1. Joke
2. Actress Gardner
3. Soap opera
4. Great anger
5. Mature
6. "You Send ___"
7. Article
8. Nocturnal bird
9. Restaurant employee
10. Naval Academy site
12. Display stand
14. Jewel
16. Plump
18. Ego
20. Statutes
21. Mastodon descendants
22. Fast plane
23. Dab of butter
25. Might
26. Wager
27. Short letter
29. Pork product
30. Head covering
33. Have remorse
35. Coarse cloth
37. Buddy
38. Brewing agent
39. Public vehicle
40. Numerous
41. Price
43. Historic period
44. Female deer
45. Past
46. Crimson
48. Letter addition: abbr.

MEDIUM

This Diagramless is 17 boxes wide by 17 boxes deep.
Starting box is on the last page.

ACROSS

1. Transcending: prefix
5. Evangelist Roberts
6. Food from taro root
9. Cultivate
10. French Revolutionary
12. Ursine "forest ranger"
14. Originated
15. Discourage
17. Main point
18. Wide-mouthed pitchers
19. Factions
20. Telegraph
21. Actress Le Gallienne
23. "The Untouchables" character
25. Luxury fur
28. Wagner opera
34. Baffling matter
35. Dagger of old
36. Female rabbit
37. Negative contraction
39. Race-car-driver Andretti
43. Aquatic mammal
44. Actor Sharif
45. Island south of Sicily
46. Requiring serious thought
47. Wrinkle
50. Relieves
51. Hodgepodge; muddle
52. Overhead railways
53. Name meaning "little one"
54. Afternoon gatherings

DOWN

1. Internal-combustion engines
2. Actor Estrada
3. Narrative
4. Associate
6. Ordinary language
7. Kilns for drying malt
8. Member of: suffix
10. Biblical gift-givers
11. Lifeless
12. Record player
13. Simplest
15. Condensed moisture
16. "Dallas" family name
19. Sensible
21. Jane Austen novel
22. Vitality
24. Sault — Marie, Mich.: abbr.
25. Move very slowly
26. California gridder
27. Sounds of hesitation
29. Within: preffix
30. Brazilian city, for short
31. Football Hall-of-Famer, Johnny —
32. Settle down snugly
33. French dramatist, Jean —
38. Christmas-song refrain word
39. Fable's concluding point
40. Pile up
41. Enthusiastic commendation
42. Provokes to wrath
43. Nebraska Indians
46. No kidding!
47. Guitarist Atkins
48. Appraise
49. Part of "to be," in Barcelona

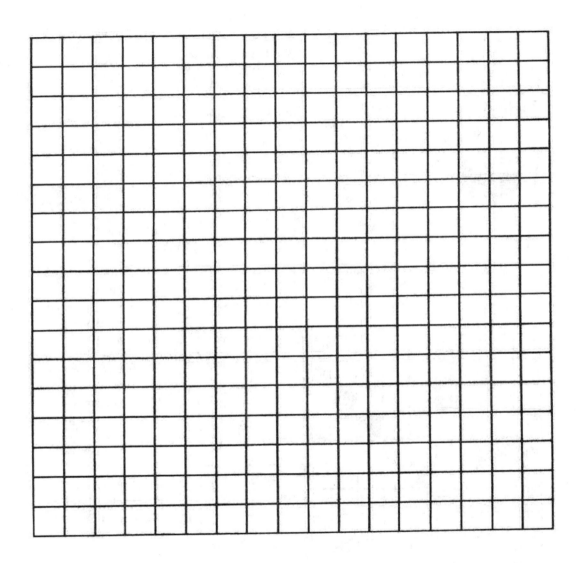

169

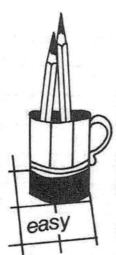

easy

ACROSS

1. Gave food to
4. Splashing sound
8. Drove fast
12. Notable time
13. Helps
14. Wan
15. — Tin Tin
16. Crimson
17. Sheriff's gang
18. Required
20. Cheer (for)
21. Paid notice
22. Goal for some high-school seniors
25. Physical discomfort
28. Rants
29. Mr. Jolson
30. Ms. Landers
31. Merchandise
32. Building wing
33. The thing
34. Looks towards
35. Region
36. Took away
38. Prince Charles' wife, for short
39. Greek god of war
40. Car shelter
44. Transportation costs
46. Wet dirt
47. Young boy
48. Lyric poems
49. Agent "007," James —
50. Thoroughfare: abbr.
51. Remainder
52. Blushing
53. Japanese coin

DOWN

1. House plant
2. Great Lake
3. Resident of Copenhagen
4. Peeled
5. Fibbed
6. Not even
7. Letter afterthought: abbr.
8. Thread holders
9. Glue's kin
10. Overhead trains
11. Actress Ruby or Sandra
17. Warsaw residents
19. Anchorman Rather
20. Roams
22. Was concerned
23. Heavy wind
24. Singer Fitzgerald
25. Set of two
26. Poker stake
27. At home
28. Competes in the "Indy 500"
31. Ocean swells
32. Kin of "uh"
34. Treed area
35. Atmosphere
37. Female horses
38. Mommy's mate
40. Firearms
41. Alack's "pal"
42. Donated
43. Eve's home
44. In favor of
45. Fruit drink
46. Cow's cry
49. Hair color: abbr.

ACROSS

1. Rodent
4. Fall flower
9. "The Princess and the —"
12. Be indebted to
13. Extra
14. Fall behind
15. Meteorologist's concern
17. Taunt
19. Crimson
20. Droopy
21. Soft drinks
24. Beauty or Trigger
25. Nautical greeting
26. Use a blender
27. Mr. Kettle
29. Take a chair
30. Kitten sounds
31. Pinch
32. Part of a Yuletide cry
33. Linger
34. Lasso
35. Velvety-petaled flower
36. Assistants
37. Greet military style
39. Recipe abbreviation
40. "To Tell the —"
41. Paper hankies
45. Goal
46. Run off to wed
48. Syrup source
49. Fabric measures: abbr.
50. Perch
51. Notable time

DOWN

1. Paddle
2. Reverent wonder
3. Steeped beverage
4. Fire leftovers
5. Raced
6. Paving substance
7. Hesitation sound
8. Goes to bed
9. Dish
10. Lessen
11. Matured
16. Cafeteria item
18. Other
20. Concern
21. "A Boy Named Sue" singer
22. Midwest State
23. Parking area
24. Rush
26. Pocketbook
27. Plumbing tube
28. Gorillas
30. Pink cinema cat
31. Signal agreement
33. Tight
34. Tears
35. Purple fruits
36. Valuable quality
37. Remain
38. Dry
39. Gratuities
41. Very
42. Employ
43. Corn spike
44. Mineral spring
47. Look!

easy

171

ACROSS

1. French artist
6. Moral principle
11. Take away
12. Head: slang
14. At home
15. Sedate
17. Mexican laborer
18. Solemn pledge
20. Bower
22. Behave
23. Cornelia — Skinner
25. Tropical fruits
27. Pronoun
28. Choir voice
30. Homesteader
32. Aided, in a way
34. Transaction
35. City on the Elbe
38. Filched
41. Pronoun
42. Composer Copland
44. Watched
45. Wonderment
47. French city
49. Crow's cousin
50. — avis
52. Mann's "— in Venice"
54. 501, in old Rome
55. Border
57. Jacob's oldest son
59. Patron saint of France
60. Mug

DOWN

1. Mean
2. Actor Marinaro
3. Man's nickname
4. Deeds
5. Bleak; desolate
6. Blessed with
7. Word in a toast
8. Short flight
9. Concept
10. Hat
11. "Duffer's" displaced turf
13. Door sign
16. Wading bird
19. Flinch
21. Marriage, et al.
24. "March King"
26. Condition
29. Fort projection
31. Bridges
33. Ridicules
35. Overshadow
36. Bounty
37. Alaskan city
39. Heavy
40. "The Mystery of — Drood," unfinished Dickens work
43. Approaches
46. Pennsylvania city
48. Printer's term
51. Woman's name
53. Vietnam seaport
56. Soldier, for short
58. Doubly: prefix

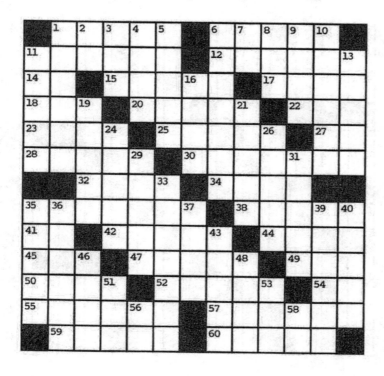

ACROSS

1. Gone by; over
5. School dance
9. Suffix with "patriot"
12. Member of the lily family
13. Emanation
14. Tropical snake
15. Iowa's capital: 2 wds.
17. Charged atom
18. Close friend
19. Experience, as freedom
21. Proposal
24. Restaurant employee
26. Expensive
27. Polite behavior
31. Aswan High —
32. Like a new penny
33. Stag's mate
34. Certain English money
36. Narrate
37. Desires
38. Quiz show group
39. Martin or Charlie —
42. Normal condition
43. Boy
44. Sam Spade, for one
50. Benefit
51. A Great Lake
52. Air for Pavarotti
53. Ironic, as humor
54. Row (of people)
55. Close to

DOWN

1. Apartment: slang
2. Malt-and-hops brew
3. Kin of "Mayday"
4. Disposition
5. Bailer's tool
6. Fast gallop
7. Metal-containing mineral
8. Great skill
9. Large wading bird
10. Chimney carbon
11. Lion's "hair"
16. Rafter's aid
20. At the stern
21. At —, quarreling
22. Notable deed
23. Renown
24. Pesos and francs
25. Suspended
27. Jaw part
28. Paradise
29. Shoe part
30. Cheer loudly
32. Willowy
35. Bread choice
36. Plaid fabric
38. Cold-weather boot
39. Fish-dinner side dish, for short
40. Tresses
41. Small whirlpool
42. Brief look
45. Memorable age
46. Pewter contains it
47. Anger
48. By way of
49. Word with "plug" or "drum"

173

ACROSS

1. Distant
4. Fault
9. Favorite
12. Frost
13. Houston athlete
14. Lyric verse
15. Opposite
17. Age
19. Pet M.D.
20. Hamster or guinea pig
21. Avarice
24. Lassies
25. Bellow
26. Taut
27. "— Are the World"
29. Likely (to)
30. Scarlet
31. Skillet
32. Exist
33. Lawn covering
35. Tie together
36. Glide
37. Beach
38. Act or react
40. Showery month: abbr.
41. Dodge
42. Saudi
46. Height: abbr.
47. More impolite
49. Possess
50. Pas' mates
51. Talk
52. Recent

DOWN

1. Evergreen tree
2. Flying expert
3. Gun the engine
4. Drilled (holes)
5. Itemize
6. Pub order
7. "Love — Tender"
8. Mistakes
9. Pontiffs
10. Biblical garden
11. Camper's shelter
16. Always
18. Not working
20. Orange peels
21. Seize
22. Heavy cord
23. Dine
24. Barnyard fowls
26. Swap
27. Magician's stick
28. Finishes
31. Brooch
33. Happy
34. Creeks
35. Fishhook end
36. Closes
37. Shooting ember particle
38. Slender shaft of light
39. Singer Fitzgerald
40. Locale
42. Summer cooler
43. Charged particle
44. Idolator's feeling
45. Compass direction
48. Skyward

easy

ACROSS

1. Taxi
4. Censure
9. Unhappy
12. Bauxite, for one
13. Document amendment
14. Fasten
15. Holds back
17. Mimickers
19. Poem
20. Sailing
21. Backbone
24. Surfer's delight
27. March
28. Equals
29. Behold's partner
30. Pub offering
31. Greek letters
32. Piglet's mom
33. Accomplish
34. Musical sounds
35. Mature
36. Everlasting
38. H₂O
39. Actual
40. Swab
41. Warning device
43. Doors
47. Stir; fuss
48. Naughts
50. River: Spanish
51. Golf score
52. On one's toes
53. Decade number

DOWN

1. Food fish
2. Exist
3. Wager
4. Wedding "costar"
5. Strong cord
6. Classifieds
7. Myself
8. Pencil ends
9. T-bone, for one
10. Broadcast
11. — Moines, IA
16. First-rate: 2 wds.
18. Pod vegetables
20. Vicinities
21. Shelter from the sun
22. Helmsman
23. D.D.E., to friends
24. Asiatic palm
25. Run away to marry
26. Oarsman
28. Of punishment
31. TV series of old
32. Pose
34. Dogwood
35. Absorbed (in)
37. "Boo-boo"
38. Least good
40. Hold in place, as a boat
41. Vital fluid
42. Woman's name
43. Before: prefix
44. Gallery display
45. Falsehood
46. Heir
49. — Paso, TX

This Diagramless is 17 boxes wide by 17 boxes deep.
Starting box is on the last page.

ACROSS

1. Theda, of acting
5. Hockey's Bobby
8. Soft cheeses
9. Sword
10. Vigor: slang
11. Provide with employees
13. Aficionado
14. Danger
15. Drink greedily
18. Contradict
19. Prefix with "eminent"
20. Half a pair, in Bonn
21. Society girl
22. Colt
23. Social insect
24. Pines
26. $1000: slang
27. Madison Avenue creations
30. Plain; stark
31. Slip up
32. Taste
33. Most urgent
34. Reo, e.g.
35. Ripened
36. Comics' Alley
39. Literary collection
40. Minister's degree: abbr.
41. Russian mountain range
43. Disburse: 2 wds.
45. Proportion
47. Herd of whales
48. Discard; junk
49. Approximately
52. Knowledge
53. Laments
54. Railways
55. Scores, in golf

DOWN

1. Phase of human culture: 2 wds.
2. Purpose
3. Congressional member: abbr.
4. Shade tree
5. Chose
6. Raised
7. Cultivate
8. Ruth's husband
9. Sixth sense: abbr.
12. Irresponsible sort: 3 wds.
13. Stokes
15. Journeys: 2 wds.
16. Cosmetic purchase
17. Start upon
19. Small openings
22. Shammed
25. Like some pitchers
27. Writers' group: abbr.
28. Moon goddess
29. Exterminators' gadgets: 2 wds.
33. Information
37. One of great wisdom
38. Go on one's beat
42. Prevaricators
44. Treat for dobbin
46. Unlock, to Keats
49. Electric unit
50. Scarf
51. Rower

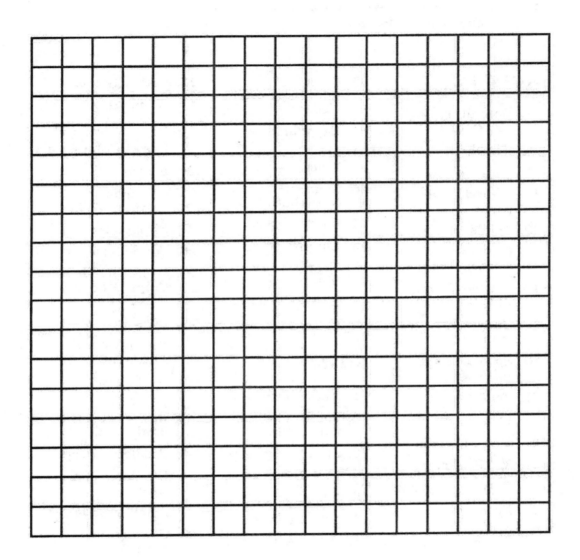

This Diagramless is 17 boxes wide by 17 boxes deep.
Starting box is on the last page.

ACROSS

1. Decorating accessories
6. Nimble
7. Latin "earth"
12. Reproductive cell: prefix
13. Taints
15. Castor's constellation
16. Marlon Brando film: 3 wds.
19. Raccoonlike mammal
20. Spaniards and Italians
21. Faulty
22. Like: suffix
23. Distant: prefix
24. Mr. Karloff
26. Draft agency: abbr.
27. Door panels
28. Certain certificates: abbr.
31. Superman's earth parents
32. Lily-family plant
33. Gary's State: abbr.
34. African country, Sierra —

35. Given in fulfillment of a pledge
38. Egyptian dam
39. See 16-Across: 3 wds.
44. Canopus's constellation
45. Incite: 2 wds.
46. Improve
47. "Blue —," 1946 film
48. Actress, Hope —
49. Fall flower

DOWN

1. Aged beers
2. South American trumpeter
3. Mock
4. Full: Latin
5. Begin: 2 wds.
7. African fly
8. Ornamental cases
9. Tease: slang
10. Brooklet
11. Novelist Seton
14. Jonathan Swift works
15. Kelly and Rayburn

16. Scholarly books
17. Acclaims
18. Back-in-style skirts
19. Russian Blues, e.g.
24. Brigands
25. Canadian province: abbr.
27. Five: prefix
28. Wind-tossed
29. "Goodbye, Mr. Chips" star, Robert —
30. Consulted
31. Southwestern Plains Indian
32. "— Fables"
34. Frank —, westerns actor: 2 wds.
35. Peddler: var. sp.
36. Old-timers, for short
37. Actor Estrada
39. City in central Florida
40. Hottentot tribesmen
41. River of central England
42. Depend (on)
43. A weekday: abbr.

This Diagramless is 15 boxes wide by 15 boxes deep.
Starting box is on the last page.

ACROSS

1. Firmament
4. Information, to a computer
8. Persia today
10. Wailing alarm
11. Cuts into cubes
13. Male felines
15. Counterfeit
16. Cereal grain
17. Insect attracted to flame
19. Unimportant facts
21. Cozy corner
23. Pace
24. Part of IOU
25. Sword handle
27. Work at (a trade)
28. Exit; "scram"
31. Car need
34. Impressionist Little
36. Mr. Garfunkel
37. "Buckeye State"
39. Cutting remark
41. Stain; blot
43. Silent pictures' Theda —
45. Exist
46. Roughen from the cold, as skin
48. Fierce North American feline
50. Wading bird
52. Commence; begin
53. Depend (on)
54. Comic, Danny —
55. Observe

DOWN

1. Comic Caesar
2. Singer Kristofferson
3. Pleasure craft
4. 10-cent piece
5. Circle part
6. Sports group
7. Actress, Susan —
9. Approaches
10. Oriental sauce: Brit.
12. Anvil-pounder
13. Threefold
14. Bend down
18. Wolf's call
20. Bride's head covering
22. Tonality
26. Paving pitch
29. Bluish-purple color
30. Reverberation
31. Chatter
32. Bedouin, for one
33. Soda tube
35. Snag or obstacle
38. Dark-yellow pigment
40. Chilly, as the wind
41. Unruly child
42. Rabbits' kin
44. Canadian province: abbr.
45. Land measure
47. Rod
49. 24-hour unit
51. Comic, Louis —

This Diagramless is 15 boxes wide by 15 boxes deep.
Starting box is on the last page.

ACROSS

1. Gift-wrapping item
4. Singer Horne
5. Actor Delon
6. Deface
9. The —, Madrid museum
10. Farm sight
11. Placid
12. *Nyet!*
14. Round handle
15. Hebrew prophet
16. English novelist, Charles —
18. At that time
19. Trivial
20. Michigan/Canada region
21. The —, Netherlands city
22. Tax expert: abbr.
25. Hawaiian veranda
26. Masticate
27. Hold sway
28. Glow
29. Forest creature
30. Frank Baum's kingdom of myth
32. Search
33. Not any
34. *"Cosi fan tutte,"* for one
36. Actress Irving
37. Fairy-tale cave-dweller
38. Biblical brother
39. Exactly suitable

DOWN

1. Necklace component
2. Shallot
3. Pale
4. South American animal
5. Songwriter, Harold —
6. Pam Dawber character
7. Medicinal plant
8. Lowe, of film
9. Walk: Spanish
10. Emulate Eric Heiden
11. Small salmon
13. Pizza spice
15. Elevations: abbr.
17. Needle case
19. Sudden, sharp pain
21. Hirsute
22. Porcelain
23. Kept in (with "up")
24. Wonder
25. Suspicious
26. Boor
27. Paper quantity
28. Turtle's home
29. Genetic material: abbr.
31. Anthony Quinn role
35. Wordsworth, for one
37. Designate, as for club membership

179

HARD

ACROSS

1. Take malicious satisfaction in
6. Diving gear
11. Carve
16. Fit for cultivation
17. Acted the model
18. Terre Haute's river
20. Best things obtainable: 4 wds.
22. Portuguese city
23. — fixe
24. Ship's cargo area
25. Western notable
27. Make lace
28. Home: abbr.
29. Vend
30. Velvety fabric
32. — noire, bugbear
33. Arm of the sea
35. Rice field
36. Feminine name
37. — Cruces, NM
38. Country estate
39. Poet Sandburg
40. Postal machine
43. Spicy meat stew
44. It's an out, usually: 2 wds.
47. Misses the mark
48. Uproar; din
50. Recent: comb. form
51. Egg — yong
52. Only
53. Wild hog
54. Military VIP: abbr.
55. Australian bird
56. Out of trouble: 3 wds.
60. Leg part
61. Cottontails
63. Love: French
64. Diminutive
65. Comedienne Tomlin
66. Weather word
67. Comic strip sound
68. Stews
70. Canea's island
71. She plays "Eunice"
75. Shade of green
76. Bell
77. Sudden burst of wind
78. Motorist's group: abbr.
79. Arab garment
80. Angling need
81. Be effusive
82. Leave speechless
83. Shorten: 2 wds.
85. Gadding, in a way: hyph. wd.
89. Heavy hammer
90. Inventor Howe
91. Mock blows
92. Slag
93. South African monetary units
94. Long, sharp teeth

DOWN

1. Certain ratings
2. Most recent
3. Woodwind instrument
4. Landon
5. Fastens, in a way
6. Incantation
7. Frigid
8. Springsteen's "Born in the —"
9. Man's nickname
10. Book supplements
11. Took an oath
12. Kola Peninsula resident
13. Nigerian native
14. Full discretionary power: 2 wds.
15. Manor
16. Blazing
19. Traveler's haven
21. Sacred
26. Some
29. European coal basin
30. Majorcan seaport
31. Extemporize: hyph. wd.
32. Cutting remark
34. Rubber trees
35. Tablet
36. City official
38. Manservant
39. Mate for "dagger"
40. Postpone
41. Fragrance
42. Pesky person
43. Enjoys a water sport
44. Knock down
45. Russian leader
46. "Goofy": slang
48. Powerful; large
49. Approximately
52. Drudges
57. Seraglio
58. Overact
59. Gardening need
60. Stitched
62. Nibble
64. Legal wrong

66. Fried batter cake
67. Set out, as on a journey: 2 wds.
68. Apartments
69. Coarse
70. Greek letter
71. Woody plant

72. Having a snack
73. Jeers at
74. Sharp tastes
76. May and Hatteras
77. Estimate
80. Bothers; annoys: slang

81. Pleased
82. Whirl
84. Tokyo, once
86. Heart of Dixie State: abbr.
87. Storage box
88. Pod morsel

180

MEDIUM

ACROSS

1. Fruit drink
4. Valuable fur
8. Portion
12. — off, print
13. Double-reed woodwind
14. Margarine
15. Displaying Chanel's creations
17. Augury
18. Foundation
19. Snow unit
20. Zeal
23. "The Raven," for one
24. Farm building
25. Criterion
29. Memorable period
30. Rugby or Soccer
31. Oolong, for one
32. Moderated
34. Outdo
35. Associate
36. Strong point
37. Sum
39. Raised platform
41. Dismounted
42. Target spot: hyph. wd.
46. Cereal grain
47. Border
48. Ship's record
49. Throw
50. Heavy metal
51. Drinking cup

DOWN

1. Prepare (for war)
2. Batman and Robin, for one
3. Terminate
4. Grinding tooth
5. Heronlike bird
6. Not any
7. Small barrel
8. Contributed to a common fund
9. One's school: 2 wds.
10. Strong odor
11. Musical sound
16. Black: poetic
19. Church bowl
20. Aid (in crime)
21. Uncommon
22. Study of theatrical arts
23. Companion, for short
25. Full of life
26. Shoe tip
27. Repose
28. Appointment
30. Vend
33. Food dishes
34. Foreman
36. Marched in a line
37. Acidulous
38. Medley
39. City fellow: slang
40. Seaweed
42. Ten decibels
43. Graceful tree
44. One of us
45. Incite to action (with "on")

ACROSS

1. Sen or piaster
5. Excel
8. Fuel
12. Forearm bone
13. Be obliged to
14. Hearty
15. Musicales
17. On the water
18. Left harbor
19. Sampled
21. Letter
22. Penny
23. Knotted
25. Exchanged
29. Vase
30. Joshes
31. Blunder
32. Improved
34. Murder
35. Crimsons
36. Devoured
37. Look out!
40. Mottos
43. Dry
44. Turncoat
46. Prong
47. Sea eagle
48. Sicilian volcano
43. Pip
50. Expire
51. Cherished

DOWN

1. Mongrels
2. Olive genus
3. Minor event
4. Tacked
5. Amphibian
6. Night bird
7. Annoyed
8. Pure
9. Malt kiln
10. Away from the wind
11. News-story opener
16. Golf mound
20. Insects
22. Tortes
23. Vat
24. Wrath
25. Abutted
26. Assign
27. Baseball statistic: abbr.
28. Wipe
30. Mock
33. Bought and sold
34. Planned and executed
36. Fruit drink
37. Cave dwellers
38. Lake
39. Beverage
40. — of Cleves
41. Poet Millay
42. Scorch
45. Silkworm

HARD

182 SPECIAL CHALLENGER CROSSWORD

by WILLIAM A. LEWIS, JR.

Here is a real toughie for you. We have omitted giving you such helps as "2 wds.," "hyph. wd.," and "slang"; but in the spirit of fair play, all abbreviations and foreign words are so indicated.

ACROSS

1. Burros, for short
6. South African people
11. Having as a foundation
16. Nimble; quick
17. Irish "oh!"
18. Puffed up (with conceit)
20. Hallstand
21. Apology
24. Put-on
25. Gasoline and Shubert
27. "How do I love thee," e.g.
28. Card game
29. Verbal applause
31. Kind of school, for short
32. Arrange in rows
33. Plays the odds
34. Word with "bed" or "home"
36. Begone!
38. Route 66, e.g.
39. Singer Crystal —
40. Stature
42. Caps; crests
44. Flammable material
45. Valid
47. Ticket
48. Keno's kin
49. Student's chore
53. The old —, Ireland
54. Congressman, at times
57. Battery substance
58. Complication
60. Instant —, on TV
62. Arizona Amerind
63. Word with "room"
64. Off-camera dialogue
66. British clock-setting standard: abbr.
67. Fraction
69. Gaelic
70. Sonoran sandwich
72. Whoopee!
73. Flowering bush
75. Large Burmese knife
77. Bath ingredient
79. Lyrics
80. Place in port
82. Sea swallow
83. Is irritating
85. Car model
87. Massachusetts dialect
91. Rodgers and Hart waltz
92. Humming, in a way
93. This group's
95. "Too Late the Phalarope" author
96. Lulu
97. Before-mentioned
98. Gazpacho
100. Have courage
101. Bout result: abbr.
102. Rigorous
104. Moving day, for some
106. Mae West role
107. Card game like 21
110. Not worth mentioning
112. Repair a boot
113. Grammatical form
114. Of a heart chamber
115. Afresh
116. Annoyingly aggressive
117. Jewish month

DOWN

1. Fill in details
2. River in Romania
3. Japanese city
4. Showed reverence
5. Arrow parts
6. Infancy
7. Sourdough's interest
8. Metric unit of work
9. Beams
10. Showdown
11. Put up, as hay
12. Old Turkish coin
13. "Pronto!": abbr.
14. Slip
15. Comics "mountie"
16. Eviction message
19. Play a flute
20. Discordant
22. Eastern Church member
23. Kind of fall
26. Scottish number
30. Wilted
33. Excellent
35. Indian Ocean sight
37. Work
38. Truck-driving contest
39. Game traps
41. Escorted
43. Game souvenir
44. Itty-bitty
46. Talks nonsense
48. Panda
49. Lampshade supports
50. Large quantity
51. Modern appliance
52. Small round hill
54. Gripper
55. Show principal

56. Scorer
59. Unisex nickname
61. Ordinary GI: abbr.
65. Like some vinegars
68. Broadway bargain
69. No gentlemen, these
71. Responsive
72. Classified
74. Rabbit or Fox
76. West German "Oscar"
78. Kitchen plastic
80. Climbers' site
81. Common pest
83. They can cause an embolism
84. Impatient motorist
85. Like dog days
86. Herder's device
88. Duse or Dante, e.g.
89. Guianan dugout canoe
90. Mournful sound
92. "Wojo's" boss
94. Moslem ruler
97. Vamp for time
99. Desirable match
102. TV static
103. Slangy number
104. So-so
105. Czarist Russian villages
108. Compass point
109. Points after deuce
111. — media

This Diagramless is 15 boxes wide by 15 boxes deep.

ACROSS

1. Drink slowly
4. Distant
7. Employ
8. Bullfight cries: Spanish
10. Shaving devices
12. Dreadful
14. Females
15. Tiny
17. Beauty shop
19. Lofty Swiss mountains
20. Zooms aloft
22. Singer Horne
23. Golly!
24. Raged
26. Gross minus cost
27. Eternal City native
29. Canonized person
31. Wooden pin
32. Look at
33. Harts
35. — on, liked to excess
37. Short swim
39. Comes back
41. Beam of light
44. Very dry
46. Rambling blooms
47. Plumbing tube
48. Underage person
50. Table support
51. Caverns
52. Suffering the effects of age
54. Made a point
56. One and only
57. Above
58. Crimson
59. Marry

DOWN

1. Small, medium and large
2. Press (clothing)
3. For each
4. In favor of
5. Cry of dismay
6. Royal
7. Picnic basket
9. Noiseless
10. Actor's part
11. Faint
12. Stipulations
13. Ice-cream container
14. Sway like a dog's tail
16. Hearing organ
18. — "King" Cole
20. Reel
21. Winter and summer
24. Smudge
25. Reducing plans
28. Choose
30. Born
33. Backbones
34. Was thievish
35. Sediments
36. Motorist
37. Water barrier
38. Eye part or spring flower
40. Utilize
42. Mimicked
43. Affirmative reply
45. Contributor
47. Peeled
49. Stir up; anger
51. Sheltered bay
53. Guided
55. Dairy animal

This Diagramless is 15 boxes wide by 15 boxes deep.

ACROSS

1. Cooking vessel
4. Weep aloud
7. Honey-loving animal
8. Lament
10. Grinds into shreds
12. Went different ways
14. Salt-water body
15. Adds spices to
17. "Merry" month
19. Apiece
21. Mixes
22. Dull person
23. Unexpected pleasure
25. Consumed
26. Trousers
27. Highway sound
29. Arches over
31. — Grande, U.S. border river
32. Period of time
33. Paid out
35. Twirls
37. Swift
39. Rodent
41. Lettuce dish
44. Unlock
45. Bats' homes
47. Rescue
48. English meal
49. Says again
51. Number of years in a decade
52. Expects with fear
54. Guiding head
56. Wise man
57. Word of dismay
58. Fiery color
59. Lock opener

DOWN

1. Pod vegetable
2. Horse food
3. Woody plants
4. Graceful water-fowl
5. Paddles
6. Nipped
7. Props up
9. Yellow fruits
10. Toothed wheel
11. Lucifer
12. — over, closely studies
13. Dash
14. Matched collection
16. Take a chair
18. Sure!
20. Coiffure fastener
22. Monkey's treats
24. Attempted
26. Home of the Eiffel Tower
28. Period of time
30. Energy
33. Lances
34. Snares
35. Pilfer
36. Blackboards
37. Decompose
38. Mimicked
40. Broad street: abbr.
42. Assert
43. Wolf's home
45. Gave up
46. Porterhouse or sirloin
49. Fury
50. Bargain event
53. Hearing organ
55. 24 hours

Answers

PUZZLE 1

```
PET.SPAR.ALSO
AVA.LAND.DEED
RIP.OLD.LOVED
ELECTS.DARE..
..AS.WATERED
CRAB.MATES.LO
LAD.PALER.ASS
AT.SAILS.FLEE
PENCILS.HA...
..ERRS.PARCEL
RAVES.HAT.AVE
AREA.SANE.PEN
GERM.ODES.ERA
```

PUZZLE 2

```
CAB.LOSE.WISP
ALA.ODIN.ARIA
PAINTEDDESERT
SNOOT.SET....
..LODI.READY
EMMA.ANTI.CIA
PAININTHENECK
ILL.NERO.IDES
CELLS.ORIG...
..YEA.CHITA
PAINTSTHETOWN
APOD.PEER.TIN
LENA.SAMS.AGA
```

PUZZLE 3

```
PEP.GRAB.SALT
ORE.RACE.TRIO
PARTAKE.SAINT
...ADE.PIRATE
GRAPE.MERE...
LONE.PARE.ASP
AVERSE.INCITE
DEW.PAIL.ODOR
...CALF.SWEPT
LEVERS.SHE...
ERODE.CHARTER
SITE.DOOR.AGE
SEES.ROPE.GOD
```

PUZZLE 4

```
AGATE.CAT.CAB
MERYL.OWE.LIE
PENNY.LANTERN
.IE.ALI.RAYS
ATE.KNITTER.
ME.TONE.ABETS
ENTIRE.MILDEW
STAGE.PALE.LA
.LEADERS.ELM
APER.ORE.AL
CENSORS.ALTER
HAT.RIO.STOVE
ELS.RAN.HONED
```

PUZZLE 5

```
TOT.SALEM.ACE
EAR.AROMA.BAA
ATE.BIT.DOLLS
.NEED.LIVELY
ALTER.HOSE...
COOL.BISON.TO
RUN.LADEN.LAW
ED.WISER.TALL
..ANTS.BANKS
GLANCE.CUPS.
RODEO.TON.IMP
AND.LEARN.NOR
YES.NANNY.GOO
```

PUZZLE 6

```
SEW.SST.STIR
NOVA.LIE.HONE
AMEN.INN.ONCE
PENTUP.ORDEAL
..ESP.ROD...
MISDEED.BYRON
ACE.RUB.ONO
DETER.DELAYED
..NIB.RAM...
ESCAPE.APPLES
ROOM.GET.EASE
ALOE.AGE.ROSE
SELL.NOD.ESE
```

PUZZLE 7

```
OAT.LOBE.SHAH
DIE.AWED.TACO
DRAFTED.WASTE
..AID.TART...
CABIN.CONTEST
ORAL.PINES.HA
MET.DAVID.BOX
IN.MAGIC.HIVE
CAPITAL.PAGES
..OXEN.FAR
TAKES.FORMALS
OVER.MALT.PEA
MARS.ANDY.TOY
```

PUZZLE 8

```
WHY.NOBLE.ASH
ROE.ONION.GUI
APART.NATIONS
PERISH.FED...
.SPEAR.ROCKS
HO.EESES.LINE
OAR.NTAIN.TOE
STAR.ELDER.WK
THIEF.METED
.NOW.STAIRS
CALDRON.LDREN
ARO.CRIME.ENO
NET.EDGES.COW
```

PUZZLE 9

```
MERCY.KABUL
MORALE.ICARUS
ID.FEAST.RAPT
DUC.WRATH.LIE
ALUM.SKEIN.NA
SELAH.INVITED
.TIED.SETA
DISDAIN.SECTS
EM.SPRAG.RORY
BAH.SETUP.SAN
AGAS.COROT.DC
RECENT.UKASES
SKEWS.SYNOD
```

PUZZLE 10

```
P A P A . . . B E T A .
P A R A D E . R E V O L T
A G E N D A . E N I G M A
T E A . . S A T . C A S T
. . . D E T R A C T . . .
R E L A X . T I E . E L I
A T O M I C . L A W Y E R
P A W . L O T . S I E G E
. . . B E T W E E N . . .
F A R E . T O T . . S I R
O V E R D O . C H E E S E
G I D E O N . H E R A L D
. D O T E . . . N A M E .
```

PUZZLE 11

```
A R K . S C A R F . C O W
D A N . T O W E R . A P E
S P E C I A L . E A S E S
. . E A R L . S I L E N T
W I L T S . C A G E S . .
A D E S . P A T H S . H A
L E D . H A B I T . J U G
L A . B E G I N . C A N E
. . W O M E N . L A C K S
S H A W L S . M A S K . .
L A S S O . C O N T E N T
A R T . C H O R E . T A R
T E E . K I T E S . S P Y
```

PUZZLE 12

```
. . . . S T O P . . . . .
. S H O W E R . . . . M E T
. T O O . E R I N . N I L E
C A R P . S I L O . S E N S E
L A C E . . L E D . T R E E
A R T . . . P R O D . . . .
S T I L L . . F E E . . . .
. S C O U T . . C A R E S S
. S U R E . B A D . T O P S
. D E N T E D . . S L A T S
. . . P I T . . . D R U M S
. . S L I P . . . . N E T .
P L A N . A S P . . S T A Y
L O A N S . S W A T . T I E R
E R I E . H A I R . A D D .
T E N . . P R I N C E . . .
. . . . S O O T . . . . .
```

PUZZLE 13

```
A L A . S L A P . A H A B
L O N . L A V A . T O R E
A S . G O C A R T . P E T
S T R I P E . . A W E . .
. . A V E . S A K E . E D
H A T E . D A V E S . V A
A L E . L A N E S . T E N
L A . B I T E S . C A N E
O N . O V E R . T A R . .
. . A B E . . P I R A T E
T O N . R E N A M E . A D
A N T E . G O N E . A P E
P E S T . O W E S . M E N
```

PUZZLE 14

```
S L O P . L I E U . G A P
S O A R . A R A N . R O I
T A K E A H A R D L I N E
. . . V C R . . E I D E R
S P R A T . B A R E . . .
A L I I . L O N G . F I T
F A L L S I N T O L I N E
E Y E . I V E S . O N C E
. . D R E D . O C E A N .
A P P A L . . B A A . . .
G E T S O U T O F L I N E
A L A . I N O N . E D E N
R E S . N O O N . S O W S
```

PUZZLE 15

```
D E D S . . . S E S S
A G E L A N S D N N N L I
H A S E N O N O E E O A I E S
R U N E R I N C W T P V K D D
F A R A A . S G E . E E E S
P A H R . . A . . E N L S
. S T . I S D R E T C N L D
. S I T T E U E A X E A E S
. R R S Y A S E E P P . R L
A A E A . N . . . E A Y L
P R L G . L G R . K U R I S
W L G T G E N O L O S E A T M
A E A O E I R A V I V T N R S
S D T T R E E V E N E E T
S S E S . . . E D G S
```

PUZZLE 16

```
. F R A M E . S I T E S .
M A I L E D . A D O N I S
A C M E . I D I O M . L P
P I E . S T I L L . S E A
L A . B L I S S . W O N T
E L . R O O K . R O U T E
. . S I G N . C A R P . .
G R O S S . R O I L . S H
L A N K . F O U N D . H O
E G G . B E A N S . M A T
A T . L A I R S . L I V E
M O D E R N . E N A M E L
. P O I N T . L O W E R .
```

PUZZLE 17

```
L O P . S L A P . S I T E
O A R . T I D E . P R A Y
S T E P O V E R . R O M E
. . . P A V E . M I N E S
S T A L E . S P A N . . .
H I R E . S T A R T L E S
E R E . B O A S T . O D E
D E S T R O Y S . A N E W
. . . R A T S . S I G N S
S T R U T . E L M S . . .
O R E S . S I D E S H O W
L I S T . U R G E . O W E
D O T S . B E E P . T N T
```

PUZZLE 18

```
A W E . C H A R . G A L A
F O X . H O S E . O V E N
T O P . I M P L E M E N T
. . . E R L E . A L E R T S
D I C E D . S T A R T . .
R O T E . O M I T . S A D
A T . D E R I V E S . L O
G A S . T I L E . E A S E
. . T E H E E . R A Z O R
S E A M E N . F E T A . .
I M P O R T E R S . L E T
L I L T . A L O E . E R R
T R E E . L I M E . A N Y
```

PUZZLE 19

```
GOER  VEAL  MAS
ALAE  IDIO  ILE
PESTERERS  SON
SAYING  SENSED
   EDIE  SOO
HEM  ONAN  TUNA
AGA  WIRED  ROD
TORE  ALBE  IWO
   YES  SRAS
VILLAS  ALLEGE
IRA  BLISTERED
SAN  LINK  DIRE
END  EDNA  SEEN
```

PUZZLE 20

```
SLED  FOAM  TOE
PARE  ANTI  ALA
ASIS  TEENAGER
SHEET  SEED
   RAH  RAPID
CONTRAST  MOVE
AVE  ALIAS  PAN
MARS  OPPONENT
PLOTS  ERE
   ATOP  EVENT
TERRIBLE  AREA
ORE  LOUD  DIAL
MAD  LEGS  ACRE
```

PUZZLE 21

```
BAR  STAMP  COO
ALA  HOTEL  RAW
ALI  ARE  ADORE
   SAME  SNOW
SPICE  SLENDER
PANT  SPITE  LO
ASS  STUDS  SEC
IT  CHORE  SOCK
NEPHEWS  COLTS
   OILS  POND
PAINT  HIM  ILL
OWN  ELOPE  EYE
WET  RATES  RED
```

PUZZLE 22

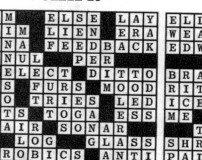

```
ASIA  SLAT  PAL
ITCH  HESITATE
DAYS  INK  RIOT
EM  ART  WARMS
   PLANT  TIP
BEAST  SUN  CAW
ADDS  GAB  POSE
YES  HOP  AROSE
   BOO  AWOKE
CANOE  ABE  SO
OVEN  ALI  VISA
RESERVED  EVER
EST  RACE  TEDS
```

PUZZLE 23

```
   GERM  MARMOT
VENUE  MAJESTY
INSET  ARAB  HR
STUD  STIR  SEA
OLE  ACHE  CORN
RESIDUE  ROUST
   OATMEAL
STRUM  AVIATOR
ERAS  STEN  ACE
RIG  PAIR  RITA
AB  ERIC  SALAD
PATRONS  OZONE
ELDEST  WERE
```

PUZZLE 24

```
TALC  BRAT  DAD
OLEO  OUCH  RIO
OPEN  ALTITUDE
   CORE  NAMES
ATHENS  EGGS
CHORE  LAS  TAP
HALT  OAR  RITE
EWE  MIX  LACES
   IDOL  TICKET
LONER  MEEK
AVOCADOS  EAST
MEN  LIST  TREE
PRE  SETS  STAN
```

PUZZLE 25

```
AIM  ELSE  LAY
TRIM  LIEN  ERA
KONA  FEEDBACK
ANNUL  PER
   ELECT  DITTO
HIS  FURS  MOOD
ADO  TRIES  LED
LOTS  TOGA  ESS
FLAIR  SONAR
   LOG  GLASS
AEROBICS  ANTI
WEE  OBOE  SCAT
ELM  TENT  EYE
```

PUZZLE 26

```
ELLA  HEAP  FED
WEAR  IDLE  RAE
EDWARDS  NOISE
   BEE  AGREED
BRAID  CLUES
RITA  ELVIS  CD
ICE  PLAIN  LOU
ME  GROWN  TONE
   TRIPS  JEWEL
SHRINE  FIN
PAINT  ALMANAC
ALE  ERLE  NOLA
ROD  READ  TWIN
```

PUZZLE 27

```
BAA  ADMIT  SEA
OIL  LEASE  WAG
BRAVEST  ERASE
   IRK  STUNTS
GRANT  BEETS
LOSE  HEARS  MA
ELK  ALL  HOP
EL  SHUTS  PARE
   POOLS  DOMES
STARTS  LIE
WASTE  MONTANA
APT  LEAVE  CUR
BEE  SHRED  TNT
```

232

PUZZLE 28

PUZZLE 29

PUZZLE 30

PUZZLE 31

PUZZLE 32

PUZZLE 33

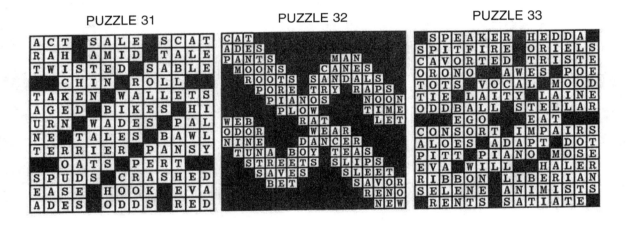

PUZZLE 34

PUZZLE 35

PUZZLE 36

PUZZLE 37

O	L	D		M	A	I	N	E		I	C	E	
M	I	A		I	N	N	E	R		F	A	R	
I	N	T	A	C	T		V	I	E	N	N	A	
T	E	A	C	H		F	E	N	C	E			
		R	I	G	O	R		H	E	L	P		
V	I	N	E	G	A	R		R	O	D	E	O	
O	D	E		A	S		S	O		B	A	R	
T	E	X	A	N		V	I	O	L	E	N	T	
E	A	T	S		M	E	S	S	Y				
		D	I	G	I	T		T	R	A	P	S	
A	B	O	A	R	D		H	E	E	H	A	W	
C	O	O		O	G	L	E	R		A	V	A	
T	A	R		W	E	A	R	S		B	E	T	

PUZZLE 38

S	T	A	G	E		S	C	R	A	W	L	S
T	A	X	E	D		P	R	E	V	I	E	W
O	M	I	T	S		R	E	V	E	N	G	E
L	A	O	S		S	A	W	S		T	E	E
E	L	M		T	H	I	S		R	E	N	T
S	E	S	S	I	O	N		B	I	R	D	S
			A	F	T		H	U	T			
S	T	A	F	F		D	A	Z	Z	L	E	S
P	U	R	E		R	A	Z	Z		O	A	T
E	R	R		F	I	N	E		A	C	R	E
A	R	I	S	I	N	G		P	L	A	N	E
R	E	V	E	R	S	E		H	O	T	E	L
S	T	E	A	M	E	R		D	E	E	D	S

PUZZLE 39

A	U	R	A	S			I	T	A	L	O	
T	R	I	V	I	A		A	M	A	Z	O	N
E	N	D	A	L	L		R	E	C	O	D	E
		I	T	A	I	N	T	O	V	E	R	
E	T	A	L		I	D	E	A	S			
L	A	K	E	S		I	S	M		S	R	O
A	B	I	D	E	R		S	A	T	E	E	N
N	U	N		N	O	G		N	E	W	E	L
		L	A	U	R	A		A	N	D	Y	
	T	I	L	I	T	S	O	V	E	R		
A	R	E	N	O	T		E	X	O	T	I	C
S	A	V	E	R	S		R	E	S	A	L	E
S	K	I	N	S			C	E	L	L	O	

PUZZLE 40

H	A	T		S	H	A	M	E		L	O	T
I	C	E		T	A	P	E	R		O	W	E
T	E	R	R	A	C	E		A	S	O	N	E
		M	A	R	K		A	S	I	S		
S	H	I	R	T		P	R	E	T	E	N	D
T	O	T	E		F	A	I	R	S		O	R
A	R	E		B	L	I	S	S		T	I	E
I	S		F	L	A	R	E		P	A	S	S
R	E	P	E	A	T	S		F	A	R	E	S
		L	A	S	S		W	I	N	G		
A	P	A	R	T		C	A	R	E	E	R	S
T	A	N		E	L	U	D	E		T	A	P
E	R	E		D	A	T	E	S		S	T	Y

PUZZLE 41

	A	V	A	N	T		V	O	L	E	S	
T	R	A	C	E	R		I	R	O	N	I	C
I	M	P	E	D	E		C	A	S	T	R	O
M	O	O	D		M	O	A	N		E	L	M
E	R	R		D	O	U	R		O	B	O	E
		C	U	L	T		A	M	B	I	T	
	A	L	A	M	O		P	R	E	E	N	
C	L	A	S	P		M	A	N	N			
L	I	R	E		B	O	N	O		O	W	N
A	M	A		I	O	T	A		G	R	A	Y
R	E	M	I	S	S		C	A	R	A	F	E
A	N	I	O	N	S		E	Y	E	L	E	T
	T	E	S	T	Y		A	N	G	E	R	

PUZZLE 42

S	E	A		G	A	L	E		S	L	A	B
O	A	R		A	M	I	D		H	I	R	E
D	R	E	A	M	E	D		D	A	N	C	E
		P	E	N		S	U	R	E			
L	A	N	E	S		S	T	E	E	R	E	D
A	L	A	S		P	O	T	S		L	A	
B	I	B		P	E	E	P	S		G	O	T
O	K		R	O	D	E		C	A	P	E	
R	E	T	I	R	E	D		L	O	S	E	S
		E	V	E	N		H	A	M			
M	I	N	E	S		C	O	W	B	O	Y	S
O	D	O	R		M	O	O	N		F	E	E
W	A	R	S		A	N	T	S		F	A	T

PUZZLE 43

A	I	D		A	M	E	N		F	R	A	Y
F	O	E		N	O	N	E		L	A	N	E
A	W	E		G	O	D		P	O	S	T	S
R	A	P	I	E	R		S	O	U	P		
		C	L	E	A	N	E	R		B	C	
B	O	N	E	S		C	O	T		L	E	O
E	R	A	S		C	O	W		J	E	E	P
L	A	Y		J	A	R		G	U	S	T	Y
A	L		B	A	N	N	E	R	S			
		D	A	M	E		M	E	T	T	L	E
B	O	O	K	S		S	P	A		R	A	W
E	L	S	E		P	E	T	S		I	K	E
D	E	E	R		R	A	Y	E		P	E	R

PUZZLE 44

G	A	S	P	E	D		B	A	R	R	E	L
U	M	P	I	R	E		O	R	I	O	L	E
S	P	A	R	E	S		B	R	O	O	K	S
		A	C	I	D		O	T	T			
B	R	I	T	T		R	A	Y	S		S	P
R	U	D	E		S	U	M	O		W	H	O
A	L	L		T	A	M	E	S		H	A	S
N	E	E		H	Y	M	N		C	O	W	S
D	R		W	I	S	E		S	H	A	N	E
			A	H	S		R	A	K	E		
E	B	B	E	T	S		D	A	S	H	E	R
B	E	E	T	L	E		A	T	T	I	R	E
B	A	S	S	E	T		M	E	S	S	E	D

PUZZLE 45

	P	E	W				F	E	D			
T	A	L	E	S			M	O	R	A	L	
O	R	A	T	O	R		P	I	R	A	T	E
N	E	T		W	A	D	E	D		S	E	T
D	E	W		T	A	R		R	E	D		
		D	A	Y		M	I	N	U	S		
		G	E	T		L	A	D				
	B	O	N	U	S		P	E	T			
T	A	N		N	A	G		R	A	P		
R	U	N		P	E	D	A	L		N	A	B
A	B	A	T	E	S		S	I	N	G	L	E
M	A	N	O	R			D	O	L	E	D	
S	A	P						W	E	D		

PUZZLE 46

```
MAP  PLOW  ATEE
ERR  LENA  SOLD
TEENAGER  LOSE
   PENS  HELEN
CHASE   SHOE
HURT  STAMPEDE
OLE  SMILE  LAY
PASSPORT  HERE
   TUGS  DOVES
AWARD   AREA
POSE  ANCESTOR
ERIE  MARS  ERA
SENT  AGES  SET
```

PUZZLE 47

```
OAT  HITS  CRAG
ALE  IDEA  RENO
KINGKONG  EDNA
   DUEL  EASEL
CHESS   PITS
HURT  LANCELOT
ALL  MARCH  EGO
PLYMOUTH  HALL
   ANDY  REPEL
CLANK   WARY
HORN  DEADBEAT
ERIE  ILKA  ADE
WEAR  PIER  ROD
```

PUZZLE 48

```
ALL  WHOM  BED
SAID  HERE  ODE
SWEETER  REIGN
   CAN  SCALES
BACKS   BOYS
ABO  KNOW  ENDS
BEND  ONE  DIRT
ELSE  TERS  NEA
   EWES  CLEAR
TRADED   PAI
WORSE  PARENTS
IAM  KILL  SORE
CRY  STEM  WOE
```

PUZZLE 49

```
HORN  PIAF  DAB
ALOE  LOCO  USA
HEISMANTROPHY
   TIN  EPEES
SPELL   HOST
HALE  TARA  DIE
ACADEMYAWARDS
DEN  PEEL  DUOS
   PINS  AMBLE
ARGOS    ALI
PULITZERPRIZE
SHE  LORE  ADEN
ERE  EONS  LAND
```

PUZZLE 50

```
DIM  SLOTS  FAT
ACE  PILOT  OUR
YES  ODD  ALONE
   SITS  PRETTY
STARS   EATS
HUGE  CANES  HA
ORE  CAGED  POP
ON  POKES  CASE
   OVER  NOSES
SHINES   HOPS
WIDER  HUT  ALE
ADE  ERASE  GAY
PEA  DESKS  EWE
```

PUZZLE 51

```
FAD  STAGE  PEA
ICE  WAGON  ALL
TEE  APE  CRISP
   PANE  SLIDES
SLEDS   STOP
HOSE  CLASS  BE
OAT  SHARE  PAL
OF  SLITS  CALM
   LOPE  ROSES
STRAWS   BOWS
WROTE  BAD  ADD
AIM  SHINE  GAY
TOP  TANGO  EYE
```

PUZZLE 52

```
   CUT  SIR
  TONE  TROT
 GRADE  ROBOT
SLATE  SIN  PEP
LOAD  ROCKY  PAW
OLDER  DOE  SPIRE
WOE  ANEW  SHADED
   TIES  DOOR
REPAST  MADE  LIP
ADORE  HAM  SPICE
NIL  LISPS  AMEN
  TEN  ASK  TAPES
 SIGNS  COVES
  PACE  OVER
   BED  PER
```

PUZZLE 53

```
EVA  SWAMP  TRAPS
AIM  TANYA  HOTEL
RAYMOND  CHAN  TO
   OUT  LION  PEP
APART  WAND  CARE
SINK  BONO  FAR
NAT  LOLA  CARESS
EN  ROOF  FORD  LA
ROBERT  BARE  CON
RED  DICK  MOOD
FRED  MILE  HAPPY
LOW  TELL  PAT
AM  TILL  WINTERS
MASON  EWING  BAA
ENEMY  RENTS  BEN
```

PUZZLE 54

```
JEER  CHAT  PER
OGRE  EASY  ADO
TOASTER  PERIL
   SEA  PRIVATE
SMEARS   ACED
MAST  TUNA  EBB
OZ  SPARKLE  OR
GET  LINE  FORE
   ROAR  REFUND
CLEANSE   ROT
HEART  REARSUP
EAT  ELLS  TESS
WKS  DOES  STET
```

PUZZLE 55

```
H A R P   O F F   C L A M
O V E R   C O O   L A N E
W A D E   C U R T A I N S
      S P U R   R I D E S
C L O S E R   M U M
R A V E N   P I E   G A P
I C E D   H A D   S A M E
B E N   T A N   M E T E R
      D A M   R E L E N T
S T R A P   S I T E
P R O T E C T S   C L I P
E A S E   O A K   T I R E
D Y E S   P R Y   S P A T
```

PUZZLE 56

```
T R A D E S   A M B E R
R E T I R E   H E A V E S
R A M   P I N T   W R I S T
C O N   E D I T   B L U E
E V E R   S P O T   M E
S E W E D   S T A G G E R
      E A R S   S T A R
H A R D I E R   S L E E T
A L   P E E L   E A V E
R I O T   S E A T   T O P
P E R I L   D R A G   L E
S N A R E S   G R I E V E
  S L E D S   E A G L E S
```

PUZZLE 57

```
A S P   S T I R   A F A R
G O O   C A N E   W I L E
A B S T A I N S   A R M S
    T A L L   T H R E A T
I M P L Y   T R U E
N O O K   F E A R   O W L
T O N   T R A I L   V I A
O D E   H O R N   R E N T
    M I S S   H O R S E
A S S I S T   P O O R
B E A N   I D E N T I F Y
L E N D   N I N E   D O E
E K E S   G E T S   E R A
```

PUZZLE 58

```
    R A Y     A H A
  M U L E S   S C A L P
T A M A L E   H E L P E R
O R B   L A K E S   I R A
M E L   L I D     N I P
  S E N S E D   A B E L
    A I D   A L E
  P U T T   C R I N G E
B A N   V A T   R Y E
A N T   P A T I O   E E L
A D O R E S   S A B E R S
  A L O N E   T R O T S
    D E S     S O S
```

PUZZLE 59

```
L A D   F E A S T   S P A
E V E   E R R O R   C A P
G A P   R A T   A D O R E
    O W N S   S P O R T S
C A S E S   M A P L E
O M I T   P A N E L   F T
L E T   B A K E D   F E E
A N   R A C E R   A L A N
    T A T E R   S N O R T
S T A R T S   A L T O
C A M E L   O R E   D A M
A L E   E N D E D   E G O
R E D   S O D A S   D E W
```

PUZZLE 60

```
O L D   S T A R E   T O S S
T E A   T I G E R   A R E N A
T A N   E L O P E   P E T A L
E S C A P E   A C H E   T I E
R E E D S   B I T E   I L L S
    D I N E R S   O D E
A P E   S E T S   P U L S E S
R E L A T E S   R A R E   D O
T R A D E D   P I N S   T E D
    T A R   C A S T   T U N A
S T E M   C A P E   D O N
L A D   P A R E   A R R E S T
A L   C A M E R A M A N   L O
B E H A V E   C R E W   D U E
    O N E   P L A N   B E G S
G A L E   C R I B   T A C
O L E   S O A P   P I R A T E
A S   H O L Y   T U M B L E R
T O W A R D   S O L E   S E A
    A R E   S T A L K S
L A T E   L O A D   E A R L S
A W E   C A R T   R E P E A T
M A R L O   T U L I P   A C E
B R E A D   E R O D E   C E E
  E D G E   D E T E R   T S P
```

PUZZLE 61

```
G E M   R A C E   F A T S
A V A   I D O L   I N I T
B A R I T O N E   E T N A
    I D E S   V A N I T Y
P A N E S   C A R D
A R E A   M A T I S S E S
P E R   T A P E D   E A T
A S S E S S E D   D A V E
    V A T S   B E S E T
A S P I R E   S I L O
L O O N   R E C L I N E R
A L E C   E T A L   E R E
N O T E   D A N S   D A D
```

PUZZLE 62

```
H O W   B A D   R O T
A M E N   L I E   R I D E
T I R E   A D D   U P O N
  T E S T S   U N D E R
    T O T   C U E
W O R S E   R E T R A C T
A R E   L I D   G U N
R E D U C E D   S L E P T
  N O T   T H E
  F A I N T   H E A R T
S I L O   U S E   D E A N
A L A N   C A R   S A L E
Y E S   E W E   P E T
```

PUZZLE 63

```
HAY STAMP   TOO
ALO HONOR   OND
ROUSE DROPPED
MORTAL EVE
  SAVED   ENDED
BE YEARS   CAVE
ERE SPICE   YEA
DRAW EVENT   ND
SARAH ENTER
  REF   DIAMON
HERSELF   CRANE
OWE LARGE   ICE
LED STOOD   DED
```

PUZZLE 64

```
RACE     SPOOLS
BEGAT BLANKET
OPERA ROLE   GO
REND ROOM   FIR
END LOOP   FROM
STADIUM PEONY
    ANT   SEA
STYLE COTTAGE
TREE WARE   BOB
RAT DONE   GRAB
ID MIRO   SAUTE
VEHICLE PIPED
ERODED   ANTE
```

PUZZLE 65

```
TILE   TSPS WSW
ADES AQUA   HOE
MATT PULP   EON
  SOD ALIMENT
COMPEER   DEL
ORA FREE   WEST
ILK TIDAL   RTE
FEES SERA   DEN
  AHA ANDREWS
BEDEVIL   SEA
RYE IRIS   CLOT
IRA OMNI   AERO
MEL NAGS   PROW
```

PUZZLE 66

```
POP SPED PAGAN LASS
EAR TIRE ORATE OMITS
PROFITED SIDES SERIAL
MAR USED THEN LIE
PLOT FACED POLAR CENT
OUT PASTE DOVES COSTS
ORE ARKS LIKED SAD
REDUCES WAVER REPEALS
RED LITER MOVE POE
BRAGS PAPER WISER ROE
RARE CATER VILER LISP
AVE DAVID HIRES MOLES
TEN OMEN CONES PAD
SLANTED TUNED PARENTS
EEL DARES SORE OIL
GROWS TIMES SHUTS TEA
OURS LOVED SHOTS MART
END SAME PIER BIB
STEAMS SALON TREADLES
SABOT THING EAST ELK
LEGS SATES DYES SLY
```

PUZZLE 67

```
TEE STAMP   SHE
AVA PUREE   LAW
PERFORM NOOSE
  URN   SNAP
PRINT WAITERS
LEND GIVES   OH
AND FADES   CUE
NE DALES   HUGE
SWEATER PAPER
  RUTS   FAR
ADOBE CARPETS
DAD SMOKE   VIA
ONE TAPES   ANT
```

PUZZLE 68

```
PUTTER   GLADES
ORIOLE RODENT
LA PLACEBO   GO
INK SCOTS   FIN
TUES TUN   MANE
ESSAYS ABUSES
  TOE     ASH
VERNAL SHEIKS
ALEE OCH   DONE
LIL LOUIS   NAT
IS PIMENTO   VT
SHEAVE TUNNEL
EAGLED OBTUSE
```

PUZZLE 69

```
RIP WAIST   ODD
ACE ARMOR   DOE
TEN DIP   ABOVE
  PLEA SCORED
PLAID CHINS
ROLE WHINE   LO
INS THING   DEN
ME MAINE   REAL
SANTA JIFFY
CHANGE COME
HOTEL CON   NAG
USA ELUDE   SPA
MEN DATES   EEL
```

PUZZLE 70

```
BED   BIAS   TWO
AVOW IOWA   HAD
RICE BULLSEYE
BLURT   SAP
  DERBY DUTCH
HER IRIS   DELI
ERA PAPER   LAD
LIMA DELE   EWE
PEARL SLABS
  TOT   PACTS
MISSOURI SOHO
ACE KNOT   SPUN
TEA SATE   EGG
```

PUZZLE 71

```
SNIP SCRAP EASEL CLAD
CODA ELATE NIOBE HALE
AMOK RACER GLOBE AIDA
DELIVERY STU TERMINAL
SANE WORLD DEER
LUSTRE CONIFER DAMASK
INLAY FAR PERON TAMPA
ADEN PAUSE DIGIT NEAR
RUE BLISTER VEXED ETE
SEPARATE LOVER DARREN
BASH REWED BITE
ALBEIT DARED CROUTONS
TYE DELED LITHIUM TOT
SOTS RELIC CURDS ETNA
ENTER THAIS LIE ELECT
ASYLUM INCITES SOIREE
VIAL TALES SING
CALENDAR TON SENSIBLE
ABED AMOUR ALONG BROW
SLOG MAORI NORSE LANE
TYNE ESSEX TWEED EYES
```

PUZZLE 72

```
HOP  SWAM  STAG
AVA  HATE  TALE
RAP  ARE  TABLE
PLENTY  SOB
   RUT  DIPLOMA
AH  NEVER  EDEN
RED  RAVEN  DAN
CRIB  LINER  LA
HOPEFUL  GUM
   TEE  SLEEPY
PLATE  SUE  TOO
AIDE  EPIC  ASK
DEER  MATT  LEE
```

PUZZLE 73

```
BAT  SWEAR  ELM
EVA  LEASE  LEE
EARLIER  COMET
   INK  HOVERS
ALONG  RIVER
LADE  FAKER  PA
AND  BAKER  TAN
SE  TRIES  BIND
   BOILS  MONEY
SHEETS  MOW
TOAST  ROLLING
ANN  LAURA  DUE
YES  EMBER  ANT
```

PUZZLE 74

```
BASIC  STOOL
LAVISH  PRUNED
UNIT  IDIOT  GA
CAD  SCENT  RED
IN  RAKES  POND
DAMAGED  BUDDY
   AMEN  DALE
SLIPS  FELLOWS
TONS  FUSES  HA
ROE  HUMID  WIT
AS  LONER  DANA
PERIOD  ELEVEN
NEEDS  SOWED
```

PUZZLE 75

```
ACME  LEI  SAMP
LOAN  ISM  ALOE
GOLD  SPA  VINE
APLOMB  GUITAR
   WOO  EGO
SEASON  SHRUBS
ALL  FEE
PLENTY  BOGOTA
   OWE  AIR
PATROL  SLACKS
AVOW  LAS  TONE
GILA  ODE  EDEN
EDDY  WET  REED
```

PUZZLE 76

```
JOB  ABLE  SWAN
AWE  NEAT  CONE
RENEGED  LARGE
   EVER  WINKED
REFER  SHE  SLY
ERIN  CHINA
DATE  HAT  SPAT
   DRAPE  SAGA
PEP  ARE  LETON
EXEMPT  TART
STRUT  CONTEST
TRIS  HONK  RUN
SALE  EDGY  NET
```

PUZZLE 77

```
JAM  WIRE  SEER
ARE  AGAR  ITSA
IND  LOINCLOTH
LOITERS  HONES
   TOD  EROS
ERAS  TSAR  GAL
POTHER  REFACE
ATE  METE  ARTE
   PEER  ERG
SHEAR  IMPROVE
HAPPYDAYS  YEA
AREA  AGRO  LES
HEEL  BEAM  ERE
```

PUZZLE 78

```
SLOB  EBBS  WIFE  BROW
PAVE  LOOP  ACID  LINE
ONE  JAYWALKER  SINCE
TARGETS  REED  BANKED
   LEE  BIND  SUNK
CAPER  FUND  HANDSOUT
ALAN  SANG  TESTS  USA
MEN  LACK  GUESS  STEP
EGGHUNT  WINDY  POSSE
   ACE  DOVES  BAD
CHUNK  JAMES  GARAGES
RANK  DOZEN  MINK  EVE
ALI  TAKEN  WARD  MAIN
BETTERED  PHIL  WORLD
   APES  PAIL  MEL
MARRED  BATS  HOLDOFF
AMAZE  FIRSTHAND  VIA
LIZA  BAKE  LANE  PANT
EDEN  ODES  EDGY  ALES
```

PUZZLE 79

```
EGO  SODA  LION
TAP  ONUS  EDGE
APPLIED  SNORE
   OILS  BUGLED
ROSES  PORT
AVID  NEIGHBOR
MET  AISLE  ROE
PREDICTS  MAZE
   ODES  CANED
BRACER  SLID
RENTS  SPANNED
ALTO  SOUP  ERA
DYER  INNS  WRY
```

PUZZLE 80

```
POP  SCALP  SHE
EAR  TOTAL  COY
PROVIDE  ELOPE
   MICE  TAILED
THINK  POSED
HOSE  PONES  BE
ALE  PALES  CAN
WE  CAPES  BAND
   WARES  MARKS
DRIVER  CANE
RIPEN  RANGERS
ACE  THOSE  RAT
WED  SIDES  SPY
```

PUZZLE 81

```
D A V I D · · S H E B A
D E V I S E · C E D A R S
E V E N · B R E · E R R O
M O N E · T O P · S N O W
A T · S O U T H · · W E ·
N E A R E R · R E S I S T
· · R O W · · · · A T E ·
L A T T E R · A V E N G E
O N · D A I L Y · · A N ·
A G E D · G O T · S O R T
V E R I · I N A · A R D E
E L E V E N · R E N D E R
· S T I N G · S A K E N ·
```

PUZZLE 82

```
R A C E · S E W S · T H O U · U S E R
I R O N · C L A P · I O U S · N E A T
P E A · M E S S E N G E R · P H A S E
S A L T I N E · C O E D · P L U M E S
· · O N E · D I O R · F E A R · · ·
S C A L E · L O A N · P L A N T I N G
W A N D · W E L L · S L A C K · T I N
A P T · D E A L · S H A M E · L E N A
Y E S · E N D · S T O N E · C O M E T
· · R A T · W H I T E · C U T · · ·
L A T E R · G R I N S · C A B · S A T
A C I D · B R I N G · B O R E · P I E
O R E · S L A T E · B A R E · S I D E
S E R E N A D E · R O S E · B O N E S
· · N A M E · C U R E · G O O · · ·
E S C A P E · H A N D · O R A N G E S
D O O M S · P A S S E N G E R · R A H
I D L E · D A R E · R A R E · H I V E
T A L L · O L E S · S P E D · A P E D
```

PUZZLE 83

```
· S E A · · · P A W · ·
· S T A R · · F I N E S
S H O V E · P R E T E N D
L A N E · L E E R · D O E
E V E · M I N E · H E R E
D E S C E N D · F A D E D
· · O R E · W O N · · ·
B R I D E · L A R D E R S
R O D E · K I N D · R A P
A P E · S E A T · P A C E
T E A C H E R · B A S E D
· S L O O P · O V E R · ·
· · S O W · · · W E D · ·
```

PUZZLE 84

```
· T A C O S · A R L E S ·
T A L E N T · N O O D L E
E R I E · R O T U N D A S
N A N · R I V E T · I N S
E W E · A P E S · B E T A
T A S T I E R · F U S S Y
· · A N S W E R S · · ·
S H A M S · H E A T E R S
T A G S · F E R N · R E P
A V E · C O L I C · R E E
G E N D A R M E · D O V E
E N D I N G · S O U R E D
· S A N T E · T R E S S ·
```

PUZZLE 85

```
A L T O · B I N S · A F T
R E I N · E S N E · S E A
T O N G U E T W I S T E R
· O F F · · S U I T S · ·
P A T I O · H E M P · · ·
A M I N · M A R I · P R O
T O N G U E I N C H E E K
E Y E · K A L E · E R A L
· · R U N S · E X T R A ·
A R I E L · B O A · · ·
S I L V E R T O N G U E D
P O L · L O O N · O B I E
S T S · E B O N · N I N E
```

PUZZLE 86

```
B A R · P I A N O · A C T
A D E · E N T E R · D O E
A D V A N C E · A B O V E
· · B A H · S N A R E S ·
S T I L L · E A G L E · ·
P O N E · R A V E L · M A
A R K · C A S E S · W I N
R E · P O K E S · W A N T
· P O L E S · C O R D S ·
S W O R D S · P A L · · ·
T A S T E · M U F F I N S
I K E · S H A R E · M O O
R E D · T O T E S · P R Y
```

PUZZLE 87

```
J A D E · B R A G · S L A B · D R E W
A L E C · A E R O · T A X I · I O W A
M I L L · L E M O N A D E S · E V E R
S T E A M E D · B O N Y · C A T E R S
· · I T S · R E N D · D U N E · · ·
B O A R S · P U R E · G R I D D L E S
A L P S · T O S S · S O O T Y · O D E
L I P · L A R K · C H O P S · C L A W
M O L L U S K · C R E S S · P A L M S
· E O N S · T R A D E · P E R I · ·
M A P L E · C H E F S · F R A P P E S
A N I L · C R U E T · M O O R · O P A
I N E · S O A R S · C O E D · O P E N
D E S S E R T S · Z O O S · R A S E D
· · E R N E · B U N S · M A T · · ·
S C R E A M · M A L T · L U N C H E S
A R I D · E P I C U R E A N · A I D A
G A P E · A R N O · O T I C · K E E L
A B E D · L Y N N · L A T H · E S N E
```

PUZZLE 88

```
T U G · D A M P · M I S C
C R I T E R I A · O N T O
H I G H B O R N · S C U D
· · R A W · · B E A D Y ·
P O K E R · H A R S H · ·
A L I A · H O R A · O A K
L I T T L E B I G H O R N
M O T · O B O L · E T T E
· Y P R E S · P A S S E ·
A S H E N · · A I D · · ·
S E A R · M A N T O M A N
H A W S · A U T O N O M Y
E L K E · S K I N · M A C
```

PUZZLE 89

```
O W E · S O L I D · T O M
F O R · A R I S E · E G O
F E A S T E D · N E A R S
· · H A S · S T A R E S ·
S I R E N · S P I T · · ·
A R I D · S P A S · B E G
L A D · H E A R T · I R E
E N S · A N T E · S L I M
· · E N D S · H O L E S ·
S T A N D S · R O D · · ·
E A S E L · R O M A N C E
A L I · E R O D E · O U R
T E A · S E W E R · T E E
```

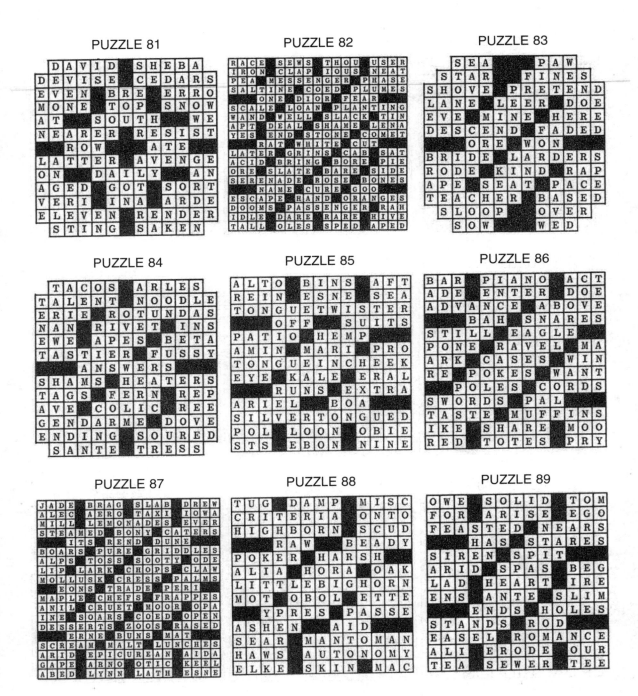

239

PUZZLE 90

```
LAP  MEET  SELL  CRAMP
ABET ALSOP PLEA  AURAE
CARRADINEADAMSGILBERT
ESTIMATE NEROS  BLEAK
DIME  TACKS  ISIS
SUEDE MICA  OVEN  MAE
DONNESMITHLENNONGLENN
UNIT ELLE  DEAR  IRED
MAT SHALE DINGY SMILE
PRESTON ALEE  BAITED
CASSAVETESRAITT
MOHAVE ROPE  WRESTED
INURE TILER SPADS ERA
FIRE ESTE  EPIS  STIR
FORDKEATSSAXONHANCOCK
SNY IRMA  SPOT  LOONS
ALAS  AFTER  ALTO
NEWTS APRON TREETOPS
GARFIELDPERSHINGDEWEY
ISSUE YALE  EERIE  DERN
GAELS EMES  NEED  DUE
```

PUZZLE 91

```
TARP  AREA  HAT
IDEA  PINS  ABE
NETTLES  SIREN
ARE  EMERALD
STRIDE  ORES
TODO  RAPT  SIN
OR TINIEST NO
PEA  MILD  RANT
DOME  SPARSE
REDNESS  AFT
ALIEN PERFUME
FIN  SOUL  IRON
TAG  ENDS  COME
```

PUZZLE 92

```
YAP  PILE  SWAB
ERA  ACID  LACE
SKILLED  HASTE
NEED  PANT
ALTAR HOTTEST
SEEP  BASES  HO
PAD  BELTS  PAW
IS  SEALS  HERE
CELLARS  SANER
EATS  BURN
SPATS PREDICT
EASE  ROAD  EAR
ANTS  EDGE  SPY
```

PUZZLE 93

```
GAG  TALON  POT
ARE  AWAKE  RUE
STOPPED  WHITE
REED  DYED
PAGES POOREST
ERIK SHORE  HI
TEA STORK  FED
AN MEANS GLEE
LARAMIE ROOTS
ERIN  WEAR
RIPEN DESTINY
ACE  AWARE  DIE
GEL  RENEW  APT
```

PUZZLE 94

```
THIRST  TENANT
EASIER ADAGIO
AW MAILMAN CT
BAA STEAM SHE
AIDS OIL AHEM
GIDEON EMBOSS
RED  OAR
SWEDEN CASTLE
NOSY ARR HEIR
AMS SPOUT NOR
CB FILTERS NO
KARATE TEETER
STATES STEALS
```

PUZZLE 95

```
TAR  FLEAS  AFT
ADE  LEAST  WAR
GAS  OAT  READY
TRAP  TEAR
SHOUT TUESDAY
TART PASTE DO
ABE HACKS SOD
RI TANKS SURE
STRIPES  EASEL
ALPS  RAMP
AGILE FIG EVA
DAN NOOSE CAN
SPY SHEER TNT
```

PUZZLE 96

```
POP  CLANG  ADD
EAR  RIVER  MAY
ARIZONA  IRATE
VEST  NOSES
ROARS  BENDS
ONTO  RODE  LO
ACE  FIRED  SAP
ME  OPEN  MONA
WIRES  CAMEL
SLICE  FORE
WADES FLASHES
ATE  TREAT  OWE
BEN  SEEPS  WEE
```

PUZZLE 97

```
CLAP SLAM MESA STOW
ROBE PACE AVID HAVE
ABUNDANT SPITE OXEN
BET ODE PULL QUAINT
ONE MORE CURL
STALE WIRE TRANSMIT
POND SALE SEATS ACE
ARE TIRE STATE IRON
REWARDS THOSE BLEND
DUE TRIPE PAL
ERODE PROPS MONSTER
RIDS DIETS HARD AVE
ADO FINES LIST OPEN
SERVANTS PEEK TREND
AMOS BATS PIE
SPICES ARCS BAN TAT
LAVA AUDIT SERENADE
IRAN USED HINT ALAN
TENT ROSE ENDS GEMS
```

PUZZLE 98

```
TAP  BLAME  SPA
ORE  EAGER  LAP
PER  ACE  RAISE
FIRE  LARD
SPEND WINTERY
LACK  WINDS  EA
ANT  PIPES  TAR
BE  SEVEN  FORD
SLIPPER  BRASS
DIPS  BOOS
SCENE  SEA  TAN
PEA  RATES  EVE
YES  START  RAT
```

PUZZLE 99

J	E	T		S	L	I	M		M	A	D	E
A	V	A		T	O	N	Y		A	M	E	N
M	A	N	S	I	O	N		T	R	E	N	D
		E	L	K		C	H	I	N			
L	E	G	A	L		S	L	E	N	D	E	R
O	V	A	L		T	I	R	E		L	A	
C	A	P		S	H	A	P	E		L	I	D
A	D		S	T	U	N			D	A	T	A
L	E	O	P	A	R	D		T	O	W	E	R
		C	A	R	T		M	O	M			
A	L	E	R	T		J	E	W	E	L	R	Y
L	E	A	K		B	A	S	E		E	Y	E
L	E	N	S		O	R	A	L		G	E	T

PUZZLE 100

P	A	S		B	A	G	E	L		T	O	T
I	N	K		A	D	O	R	E		I	N	N
E	D	I	T	S		T	I	N		N	E	T
			O	I	L		E	D	G	E		
P	A	L	A	C	E	S		E	A	S	E	D
O	W	E	D		M	A	R	R	Y		L	A
S	A	D		L	O	V	E	S		B	A	R
T	I		P	A	N	E	L		D	A	T	E
S	T	E	E	D		D	A	M	A	G	E	S
		L	A	D	S		Y	E	T			
A	L	L		E	E	L		T	A	S	T	E
F	E	E		R	A	I	S	E		A	I	L
T	E	N		S	T	E	E	R		G	E	M

PUZZLE 101

L	A	G	E	R		M	A	Y	A	N		
N	E	V	A	D	A		A	T	O	M	I	C
E	V	I	L		R	A	Y	O	N		M	R
H	A	D		B	E	B	O	P		F	R	A
R	N		S	O	B	E	R		C	L	O	T
U	T	E	N	S	I	L		S	L	I	D	E
		B	O	U	T		O	P	E	C		
S	H	O	W	N		S	P	A	R	K	L	E
P	O	N	Y		B	L	O	C	K		A	X
A	M	Y		G	U	I	S	E		T	N	T
R	I		G	I	R	D	S		S	A	A	R
K	N	E	E	L	S		U	T	O	P	I	A
Y	A	L	T	A		M	O	S	E	S		

PUZZLE 102

P	A	T		A	P	P	L	E		O	N	E
E	R	R		F	L	O	O	R		D	A	Y
P	E	A		T	O	T		E	L	O	P	E
	C	R	E	W		S	C	O	R	E	S	
M	O	T	O	R		H	A	T	S			
A	H	O	Y		C	A	V	E	S		H	I
S	I	R		D	A	R	E	D		P	A	D
K	O		H	I	R	E	S		F	I	L	L
		A	N	T	S		P	A	S	T	E	
S	T	A	I	N	S		W	A	N	T		
C	A	B	L	E		T	I	P		O	W	N
A	L	L		R	A	I	S	E		L	E	E
T	E	E		S	H	E	E	R		S	E	T

PUZZLE 103

P	A	R		S	H	A	M	E		T	S	E
I	C	E		C	E	D	A	R		A	I	L
P	E	S	T	E	R	S		R	A	S	P	S
		T	I	N	S		W	A	N	T		
T	H	E	R	E		S	I	N	N	E	R	S
R	O	D	E		S	O	L	D		D	O	T
A	M		D	E	A	R	E	S	T		B	Y
M	E	T		A	G	E	S		H	E	E	L
P	R	E	S	S	E	S		R	I	N	S	E
		N	U	T	S		C	A	N	T		
G	L	O	B	E		D	A	R	K	E	S	T
A	I	R		R	A	I	S	E		R	U	E
L	E	S		S	T	E	E	R		S	E	E

PUZZLE 104

E	R	A		S	A	G	A		S	H	I	P
V	A	T		C	L	A	N		T	A	R	A
E	T		T	O	A	S	T	S		R	E	D
R	E	A	S	O	N			T	I	P		
		M	A	P		S	E	E	N		S	C
B	E	E	R		S	E	V	E	N		P	A
R	I	N		C	H	E	E	P		P	I	N
O	R		C	H	U	R	N		H	O	N	E
W	E		O	A	T	S		W	E	D		
		T	O	M		S	E	A	S	O	N	
A	D	O		P	O	S	T	E	R		M	E
D	O	N	E		R	E	A	D		B	E	E
D	E	E	D		E	A	R	S		E	N	D

PUZZLE 105

G	A	Z	A		L	E	A	P		L	A	W
E	G	O	S		E	R	L	E		A	L	A
L	O	O	K	I	N	G	B	A	C	K	O	N
		A	C	T			C	R	E	E	D	
J	E	N	N	Y		P	L	O	Y			
E	R	I	C		A	L	E	C		D	P	S
T	A	K	E	A	B	A	C	K	S	E	A	T
S	S	E		T	E	C	H		E	L	L	A
		E	T	T	E		A	L	I	E	N	
A	G	I	L	E		A	L	L				
B	A	C	K	S	A	N	D	F	I	L	L	S
C	P	O		T	R	O	D		N	O	S	E
S	E	N		S	E	W	S		G	A	T	E

27-Across: displaced persons

PUZZLE 106

S	A	W		S	L	A	Y	E		F	A	R
I	R	A		H	O	N	E	Y		L	I	E
T	E	S	T	I	F	Y		E	W	A	R	D
			A	N	T		E	L	A	M		
S	H	A	K	E		F	A	I	R	E	S	T
T	A	L	E		B	I	R	D	S		T	O
A	S	K		T	E	N	T	S		H	O	W
I	T		S	I	R	E	S		L	I	N	E
R	E	S	T	L	E	D		W	A	T	E	R
		H	E	L	D		R	O	W			
S	H	A	P	E		P	E	R	S	O	N	S
H	E	M		T	R	E	A	D		W	O	E
E	R	E		H	A	N	D	S		E	W	E

PUZZLE 107

A	L	P		S	T	A	M	P		S	A	T
S	E	A		C	A	N	A	L		L	I	E
H	A	R	V	E	S	T		A	C	O	R	N
			T	A	N	K		S	T	O	P	
A	R	I	S	E		T	A	T	T	E	R	S
T	O	N	E		C	A	V	E	S		O	H
T	U	G		B	A	K	E	R		C	U	E
I	T		P	O	R	E	S		C	A	S	E
C	E	L	L	A	R	S		B	O	N	E	R
		E	A	S	Y		L	O	A	N		
G	R	A	N	T		G	A	L	L	O	P	S
O	U	R		E	L	E	C	T		N	A	P
D	E	N		D	O	M	E	S		S	L	Y

PUZZLE 108

```
    P I N
    O D O R         B O W
    D O M E         T I D E
    L A S   D A R E D
    D E P E N D S     D A Y
    N I C K S       W I S E
  F A S T E R     Y A N K S
  W I P E   R E D   O N E S
S I N E W     A R G U E D
O R E S     B A S E R
B E D   R E N E W E D
    M O A T S     E R R
    E L S E     T E A R
    N E T     S A G A
            M E T
```

PUZZLE 109

```
W A N T E D     S P R A W L
O R A N G E     T E E P E E
N O   T A N     A N T   A N
D U B   D I L L S     A S S
E S A U   A I L   F L E E
R E N T A L S   G U L L S
      T I S S U E S
S W E E T   O N E S I D E
T H A R   P M I   Y A R N
A I R   M E E C E   N A G
L N   N O O   O L D   P I
I N T E R N   R I D D E N
N Y L O N S   N A T U R E
```

PUZZLE 110

```
M E T   S H A M E   S O B
A R E   T A P E S   C U E
P R E P A R E   C R A T E
      O N E   C O A L
S C A L D   C O R R E C T
T O L L   S L A T E   H I
O L E   B O A T S   T A G
L A   B A R N S   L O S E
E S T A T E S   B O N E R
      A R T S   H E N
A R I S E   D A N G E R S
V A N   R O U N D   V I A
A N T   S H E D S   E G G
```

PUZZLE 111

```
A M P   S C A R F   S E W
L E O   H O V E R   T R A
F L O R I D A   I T A L Y
    D O N E   S N A R E S
S A L L Y   B O G I E
N O E L   M O D E L   G O
I N S   S A L A D   M A R
P E   S L I T S   S A L E
  L I E N S   P O L E S
S T A T E S   O R A L
C R I S P   E V E R E S T
O U R   E L V E S   T A R
W E S   R O A R S   S P Y
```

PUZZLE 112

```
C A T   P A L M   S H O P
U S A   A W A Y   T O N E
P H R A S E S   W A T E R
    I T S   L I N E
P A N D A   R I D D L E S
A L A S   S A V E S   L A
R O B   W O V E N   W A G
I N   S A L E S   D A T E
S E C T I O N   M I X E S
    H A T S   H U M
B R A G S   D E F E A T S
E A S E   W O L F   S I P
E Y E S   E N D S   K E Y
```

PUZZLE 113

```
S C A M S     B A S I S
C A D R E   A R R E S T S
A R I S E   M I N A R E T
D O E   P R I M O   A R A
S N U B   I N S   V E I N
      A M M O   B E L L S
  D U N E S   D I X I E
P E N A L   H U G E
O P A L   B O B   D A S H
S O W   F I R S T   F O E
T R A V E L S   A L I B I
S T R A N G E   P A R E S
S E N S E     E X E R T
```

PUZZLE 114

```
P E R   C H O P S   W O W
A L I   H O I S T   A V A
M I C H A E L   R A V E D
    H A R D   W A D E R S
S T A R T   S E N D S
C U R E   S N A G S   L T
A N D   S H O V E   P E A
N A   S C O R E   A L A N
  S P A R E   F R A N K
C R E A T E   T E E N
H E A R T   A R R A N G E
E A T   E L L E N   E O N
T D S   R O L E S   R O D
```

PUZZLE 115

```
J A M   C A L M   S L E W
A V A   A R I A   P O L E
R E G A R D E D   E A S E
    I N T O   F A M E D
P A C T   R A D A R
A R I S E   C O D   S P A
S E A   R O U T E   H I P
T A N   R A T   D R O N E
    P O K E S   A V E R
L A T E R   P A N E
O M E N   T R I C K L E S
S E N D   W A N E   E R A
E N D S   O W E S   D R Y
```

PUZZLE 116

```
F E L L   M A R   P R E P
A L A I   A P E   R O A R
C I N N A M O N   E L S E
T A C K L E   D U D L E Y
    E S E   D E S I
H A L   S C A R E C R O W
A L O E   L I E   T E R I
H A T F I E L D S   D O T
    F R A Y   O A R
C A R E E R   B U N Y A N
E R I C   C O O L I D G E
L I N T   U R N   S E A T
L A D S   T E E   E R R S
```

PUZZLE 117
```
DIAL  RAPT  ALP
ROLE  ELIA  PEA
UNSYMPATHETIC
     TAUNTON
SUREST  SEDATE
ALA  EER  ELOD
UNDERSTANDING
NAIL  SBA  ETE
ARIOSO  RHINOS
    PASTEUR
QUIETASAMOUSE
UNS  EGIS  NDAK
OER  DENT  YOKE
```

PUZZLE 118
```
ALP  ACTOR  COW
GEE  BRAKE  AVA
ODD  OAR  TAPER
   DRUM  SIRENS
ALLOT  FORMS
REED  TALES  BE
EAR  FILES  SEA
AN  TOLLS  MASS
  MILES  PARTY
SPILLS  BIND
HELLO  PAN  IRE
OAK  WHERE  NOW
PRY  SOAKS  EYE
```

PUZZLE 119
```
LAP  TRAP  ALAS
EVA  HOLE  TILE
DARKENED  TRUE
  AIMS  DREAMS
LADLE  ALAN
EVIL  AMENDING
SOS  EVERT  TOE
SWEETENS  LENT
   DONS  DIMES
MOWING  MINI
EPIC  EBENEZER
TENT  RARE  EGO
ENDS  STER  SGT
```

PUZZLE 120
```
HAH  TACIT  ARM
AGO  ILONA  NEE
SAUNTER  BANAL
  DOLE  ALBERT
SHINE  SIOUX
PANE  AUDIT  PO
ALI  GREED  CUB
NO  FEUDS  FORE
  MAYBE  LORRY
ODESSA  ALAN
TASTE  ABOLISH
ITS  RUGBY  COE
SAY  SPEED  ELM
```

PUZZLE 121
```
FAN  OPERA  PAS
ICE  BALES  AIL
TEETERS  SORRY
  DESK  PURE
FALSE  PARASOL
ABET  BAGEL  LA
TIS  TONES  SIP
ED  SHAGS  DIVE
DEBTORS  CAMEL
  LAUD  WARM
STING  CONTEST
PAN  HEARD  RUE
AND  TARDY  SEE
```

PUZZLE 122
```
RID  SAME  COME
ONE  AMEN  AWAY
ATE  MEET  ENDE
ROPES  KEYS
   TOO  REARED
FRIENDS  TRADE
EAR  DAN  SEA
AROSE  DESCEND
RENOWN  WHO
   READ  INNER
HAIR  MOTE  OWE
ALSO  EVIL  TEN
SLEW  SEND  EST
```

PUZZLE 123
```
  RAM     SHE
  ATE     TEN
 STORM  GRADE
HAT PEA RUT RAG
ALAS SPAT PANE
METE STAY WASTE
 EASTER  FINE
   PER   HIS
  SEEM  DIVERT
SWORD RUDE IRIS
LORE FIND PACE
YET MAT ERR DEW
 STOLE  NOOSE
  ADS    ADO
  TEE    DEN
```

PUZZLE 124
```
      TAP
     CARES
    COMMENT
   BORE  POEM
  LOVED  SWEET
 PINE      MARS
 SANER    SLAPS
 EGG        PEA
 WEEKS    HOPED
  DRIP    OWED
  STOPS  SCOLD
   ERIE  LAPS
    TELLERS
     SLIPS
      SET
```

PUZZLE 125
```
DAGGER  SLUMPS
ETOILE  HONSHU
IT  LAPLAND  ON
SIC  NOISE  AND
TRAM  SET  AVER
SEVERE  ARGOSY
  ORA     ARC
BARGES  STEALS
ESTE  WET  EDIT
ASS  COLAS  ONE
SO  ARRIVAL  DR
TRIPOD  ELEVEN
STOOPS  SERENE
```

PUZZLE 126

```
SIR_PANIC_PIG
ORE_ALONE_ALA
DAMAGED_NAILS_
__OWES_STUN__
SAVES_COUNTER
ABES_SHIRT_LO
LOS_DAILY_SUB
TV_BALLS_FADE
SECURED_BONES
__ASKS_CUED__
WASTE_PASSAGE
AGE_NURSE_LOB
SOS_SPOTS_SOB
```

PUZZLE 127

```
BIB_CRIB_GROG
ARE_HERO_AIDE
YANKEES_RIVET
__EEL_MINA___
TRUNK_PANELED
HART_REDD_LO
ICE_GUESS_ADD
NE_SANE_GREG
GREMLIN_FLARE
_DIET_LOU____
BAWLS_VARMINT
ODIE_MART_LEO
BOND_ANDS_KEY
```

PUZZLE 128

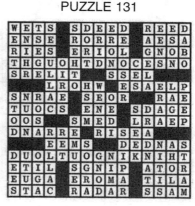

```
SIP_PACES_CAT
ARE_ADORN_AVE
PAPER_PRO_DAN
__RED_SOME___
STRIDES_PETIT
IRON_MODEL_RI
RAT_CORED_PER
ED_PANEL_SANE
SEVEN_SAMPLES
__ANDS_YOU___
WIN_LOT_WRITE
ACE_ERODE_ROY
YES_STOOD_EWE
```

PUZZLE 129

```
PEP_CHOP_CLAN
ARE_HOUR_LONE
SIR_INTO_OATS
SESAME_PLANET
_USE_PEAK____
SOAP_SORT_MAT
ADD_SPITE_ORE
GEE_POSY_CUTE
_AONE_RUN____
HEARTS_BUTTER
ACRE_OPAL_ATE
THIN_RISE_INN
SODA_SEER_NAT
```

PUZZLE 130

```
LET_SCOLD_CAB
ARE_CANOE_ALA
PREPARE_BONER
_ART_CARESS__
STAGE_MATES__
LACE_TAPES_DO
IKE_LIKES_RID
ME_RIDES_LOVE
_CASES_CODES_
SPLITS_BUN___
ERODE_TARGETS
LAS_NOOSE_NAP
LYE_SHOES_DRY
```

PUZZLE 131

```
WETS_SDEED_REED
ENSE_RORRE_AESA
RIES_ERIOL_GNOB
THGUOHTDNOCESNO
SRELIT_SSEL____
_LROHW_ESAELP
SNRAE_SEOR_RAE
TUOCS_ENE_SDAGE
OOS_SMED_LRAEP
DNARRE_RISEA
_EEMS_DEDNAS
DUOLTUOGNIKNIHT
ETIL_SGNIP_ATOR
EUGA_EROMA_TILA
STAC_RADAR_SSAM
```

PUZZLE 132

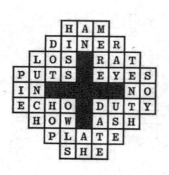

```
    HAM
  DINER
 LOS  RAT
PUTS  EYES
 IN     NO
ECHO  DUTY
HOW  ASH
 PLATE
  SHE
```

PUZZLE 133

```
GARB_LAWS_SAW
AGAR_ALOE_OLE
BONECHINACUPS
_NOR_WORST___
MOODY_SLAG___
ASTA_ITER_COB
CHINASYNDROME
HAS_LILT_EDEN
_BASE_BLAND__
SCRUB_BOA____
CHINACLIPPERS
OAF_MAIN_SNIP
TNT_ANTS_EDDY
```

PUZZLE 134

```
_TEPEE_CHAIR
MURALS_HITTER
ACID_SHADE_SO
USE_LEASE_BUD
NO_GENRE_POLE
AN_RACE_MOTTO
_WAVE_BOSH___
SPICE_CANS_CB
TINE_MELEE_RE
END_DILLY_LET
AT_DITTO_MEAT
MOTIVE_TWENTY
SONAR_SENSE
```

PUZZLE 135

T	O	P		D	A	M		E	C	L	A	T
A	M	O		A	G	O		T	R	I	B	E
C	A	S	E	Y	A	T	T	H	E	B	A	T
T	R	E	N	T		T	H	E	M			
		A	I	T		E	L	O	I	S	E	
A	C	T		M	E	I	R		N	O	U	N
T	H	E	B	E	L	L	O	F	A	T	R	I
H	E	A	R		S	O	S	O		A	D	D
A	F	L	O	A	T		E	R	A			
			I	D	A	S		E	S	T	E	E
C	H	I	L	D	R	E	N	S	H	O	U	R
P	A	N	E	L		B	U	T		A	R	I
A	W	A	R	E		A	N	S		D	O	N

30-Down: International Labor Organization

PUZZLE 136

N	E	T		C	A	R	E	D		C	A	T
A	V	A		O	L	I	V	E		O	R	E
B	A	R	O	N		G	E	L		M	E	N
			M	E	T		R	I	P	E		
P	L	E	A	S	E	S		V	E	S	T	S
R	E	A	R		N	E	W	E	R		O	H
O	A	T		S	T	A	I	R		A	W	E
P	S		L	A	S	T	S		S	L	E	D
S	T	E	E	D		S	E	T	T	E	R	S
		R	O	D	S		N	E	E			
I	D	O		L	A	P		S	P	A	D	E
R	E	D		E	V	E	N	T		L	A	Y
E	W	E		S	E	N	D	S		A	D	E

PUZZLE 137

G	R	E	W		P	E	W		P	R	E	P
L	A	V	A		A	G	E		R	O	A	R
A	C	E	S		N	O	T		A	L	S	O
D	E	N	T	E	D		T	A	I	L	E	D
			E	R	A	S	E	R	S			
S	P	A	D	E		A	S	C	E	N	D	S
A	I	D		T	N	T				A	Y	E
M	E	D	D	L	E	D		E	A	G	E	R
			R	E	A	S	O	N	S			
P	O	N	I	E	S		P	E	T	A	L	S
O	V	E	N		E	V	E		E	R	I	E
P	E	A	K		R	A	N		R	I	P	E
E	R	R	S		S	T	S		S	A	S	S

PUZZLE 138

D	A	L	I		T	Y	P	E		P	A	W
O	M	E	N		H	E	I	R		I	C	E
V	E	N	T		I	N	N	O	V	A	T	E
E	N	T	E	R	S		E	D	E	N		
			N	U	T	S			E	X	I	S	T
S	E	N	S	E	L	E	S	S		S	E	A
T	R	U	E			E	A	T		S	T	E	W
A	I	M		A	S	T	E	R	I	S	K	S
R	E	B	E	L		S	P	O	T			
			N	E	E	D		H	E	D	G	E	D
O	V	E	R	R	A	T	E		O	L	E	O
W	A	S		T	M	E	N		W	E	L	L
E	N	S		S	P	A	S		N	E	S	T

PUZZLE 139

A	B	L	E		S	H	O	E		A	N	T
D	E	A	R		E	A	R	S		C	O	O
D	E	P	A	R	T	S		C	A	R	E	S
			S	O	S		C	A	M	E	L	S
S	H	R	E	D		T	A	P	E	S		
T	O	A	D		G	I	V	E	N		H	I
E	L	M		O	N	E				P	O	D
W	Y		C	H	A	T	S		M	I	L	L
		R	O	O	T	S		H	A	N	D	Y
S	H	O	O	T	S		J	A	R			
L	A	D	L	E		T	U	M	B	L	E	R
A	L	E		L	A	W	S		L	A	V	A
B	O	O		S	L	O	T		E	D	E	N

PUZZLE 140

M	O	O		P	A	T	H	S		S	I	P
A	I	R		A	N	V	I	L		T	A	R
P	L	E	N	T	Y		K	I	M	O	N	O
			G	E	T		D	E	M	O	N	
S	H	O	W	E	R	E	D		L	E	S	S
H	E	N		R	A	P		R	E	S	I	N
A	L		I	N	H	A	L	E	S		N	E
L	E	A	N	S		R	I	P		A	G	E
E	N	D	S		S	T	E	A	D	I	E	R
		M	E	E	T	S		I	N	S		
W	A	I	T	E	R		O	R	A	L	L	Y
A	C	T		L	A	I	N	E		E	Y	E
Y	E	S		S	P	E	E	D		S	E	T

PUZZLE 141

R	A	N		S	L	E	D		S	T	E	P
I	D	O		H	A	L	O		H	A	V	E
P	E	R	F	O	R	M		R	I	S	E	N
			A	R	K		P	O	E	T		
S	H	A	D	E		T	A	L	L	E	S	T
T	O	R	E		L	A	C	E	D		H	I
A	N	T		R	O	P	E	S		R	A	M
K	O		S	A	V	E	D		L	I	V	E
E	R	U	P	T	E	D		R	A	G	E	D
			R	E	E	D		S	O	D		
P	A	G	E	D		S	T	A	Y	P	U	T
A	G	E	D		L	E	A	D		U	S	E
N	O	S	Y		O	A	R	S		T	A	N

PUZZLE 142

	C	O	P	A	L		L	I	M	I	T	
S	A	L	A	M	I		A	N	O	D	E	S
A	V	I	D		S	O	S		B	E	A	T
R	I	O		A	B	A	S	H		A	B	A
I	T		E	M	O	T	I	O	N		A	S
S	Y	L	V	A	N		E	N	O	U	G	H
		E	A	T				O	S	S		
D	U	N	D	E	E		E	R	E	C	T	S
U	N		E	U	C	H	R	E	D		A	T
A	I	M		R	H	I	N	E		D	I	E
N	O	A	H		O	D	E		H	O	W	E
E	N	S	U	R	E		S	P	I	R	A	L
	S	T	E	E	D		T	I	T	A	N	

PUZZLE 143

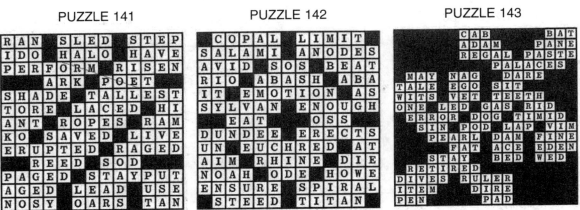

PUZZLE 144

```
ILL  STRAP  LAP
TEA  TEASE  ODE
SIXTEEN   RAVEN
    HEM   SIDE
STEAD  FLOODED
IRAN  RAIDS  LO
LET  CORDS  TOM
LA  FRAME  TAPE
STREAMS  SIRES
   OLDS   BED
STALL  CAVEMAN
HES  ERASE  OWE
YET  SIREN  PET
```

PUZZLE 145

```
TAPER  HOT  APE
ABOVE  ARE  SAD
METES  WEE  PSI
   NICKS   WEST
ARC  NO  MANES
DOOM   RECUR
EDGE  ERA  EVES
   RIDER   SOLE
SATIN  EM  WIT
ALIT   LATER
TIN  TAB  LARGE
ACE  ONE  OCEAN
NED  WED  NESTS
```

PUZZLE 146

```
NAP  FLOAT  EGG
EVE  LEASE  VIA
WAR  ANT  REALM
   FAST   CRADLE
FRESH   TEASE
LACK  REACT  DO
ART  SENSE  PEA
WE  CHASE  WANT
   SHADE  MIRTH
VANITY   TINT
ERECT  LAX  NIP
SEE  ELOPE  ERA
TAR  RATED  RED
```

PUZZLE 147

```
LAIR  LEI  HALF
ECRU  ERN  AGIO
STANDARD   DOVE
   SOP   IMAGES
ARGOT   SCAR
GURU  SPATULAS
ADIT  WIT  NAME
RENOVATE   INON
   FILE   SNERD
MORTAL   MAW
ALAI  ORATIONS
SLIM  WAN  THAI
KANE  SPY  HOPS
```

PUZZLE 148

```
SCRAP  CRAM  BUSH
IRATE  RIDE  ASIA
TOKEN  ABET  GUNS
EWE  CAN  PET  ACT
MINK   TROLLEY
STOOL        MY
NUMB       EDGE
ONE         RAW
WANE       FAME
   GO      COWER
KINGDOM   DOOR
ADE  EVE  WHY  LOT
PEAL  ELSE  OLIVE
PARE  REAL  TAKEN
ALSO  TELL  EXERT
```

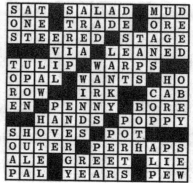

"Oh, my kingdom for one pencil!"

PUZZLE 149

```
DAM  SLAB  FLAG
ICE  PONY  REDO
DESSERT   MOVED
   SAND   GONE
SLANT  PROTEST
WAGE  CLASS  NO
ATE  SHAPE  CAT
ME  SLATE  CARE
PROMISE   ROLES
   RIPE   TALL
OPALS  PUTDOWN
DATE  LANE  FOE
DYES  ORES  FEW
```

PUZZLE 150

```
ABE  SPADE  SLY
SON  TONIC  POE
HOLLAND   ONION
   AIRY   SNACKS
CORKS   STOVE
URGE  ROOMY  GM
RAE  RAINY  GOO
EL  TITLE  WRAP
   FINES  BAILS
CLINGS   RUIN
RURAL  PARTNER
ALS  ELECT  ERA
BUT  TONES  DRY
```

PUZZLE 151

```
SAT  SALAD  MUD
ONE  TRADE  ORE
STEERED   STAGE
   VIA   LEANED
TULIP  WARPS
OPAL  WANTS  HO
ROW  IRK  CAB
EN  PENNY  BORE
   HANDS  POPPY
SHOVES   POT
OUTER  PERHAPS
ALE  GREET  LIE
PAL  YEARS  PEW
```

PUZZLE 152

```
GILA  AHA   ADD
ERAT  ROI  BLUR
NAIL  RUMPOLES
   NAST   ATTAR
RESTSTOP  OSLO
ACTA  ENE  NEED
SHAH  ROADRACE
HORAE   ISEE
   TWO  LARDNER
MARKSMEN  SAVE
IDES  ART  OVEN
OAK  ESS  XENO
```

PUZZLE 153

```
SHE  SAAR  STEW
HAD  EDNA  HIDE
AVE  COD  RANGE
MENTOR  TIP  ED
  ONESIDED
UPEND  ADE  EAT
SAVE  STY  TAPE
EYE  SHY  SIREN
  RETURNED
AD  VAN  ENERGY
VIPER  AVA  IRA
ERIN  ABET  SOL
RENT  MERE  EWE
```

PUZZLE 154

```
      LOP
     DOVER
    LIBERAL
   COVER  PEN
   ROVES VITAL
 CAVES  GOD  TIP
 AGED  MOW  TUNA
 NET  CAT  DIRER
   SEVEN SALAD
    DAD  MOTEL
     TAMALES
      RAZED
       YES
```

PUZZLE 155

```
CAP  CATER  COT
ODE  ADORE  AWE
DONOR  TIM  DEE
    WED  NOTE
SLENDER  VOTES
TONS  NOSEY  VA
ROD  STOPS  RAN
AS  PASTE  WADE
PECAN  SLEEPER
    ALDA  LAP
FOG  ALA  STUNS
IRE  LEDGE  SEA
BED  SEEPS  EEL
```

PUZZLE 156

```
MAID  PAS  SHOT
AXLE  LIT  HOPI
TEEM  ALA  ROAD
ASSAYS  NEEDLE
   NET  DMD
HURDLES  ASPEN
USA  PREEN  IWO
TENSE  TRANCES
   ART  ATE
ADVISE  SEAMEN
RAIL  ARE  RILE
ARNO  SIR  ELSE
BEER  EDS  READ
```

PUZZLE 157

```
SOMALIS  SHALE
FLUIDITY PARENT
RATLINES ONEIDA
INMATE  TARS  SUN
ETON  PEST  MURK
RED  FARMS  CORES
DELANO  ABATES
  ATOM  SANE
ERNANI  SLOTHS
IDEAL  STILE  ELM
MUNI  MEAN  KNEE
ACT  DODO  STEBER
MAILER  INTIMATE
STEELS  SEALANES
ERNIE  MOTTLED
```

PUZZLE 158

```
  MAP  TOAST
CORES  HANDOUT
ATONE  APED  NO
SOS  WARES  ANT
TREE  RED  FLEE
   LOTS  BOILS
  STUDY  HURTS
SHADE  RENT
CAKE  BAR  SAFE
ORE  FAVOR  LAY
UP  CASE  ALIKE
RELATES  PACED
RATES  WED
```

PUZZLE 159

```
 SCAMP  SPAIN
SHOWER  KOWTOW
OR  EMOTION  TO
LIT  OTHER  RIM
ONUS  EAR  MICE
NEGLECT  WIDEN
  BOLT  BAND
BROOM  GORILLA
LEAP  CAR  MEAN
ACT  PRIED  SUN
SO  SLENDER  RA
TRYOUT  OLIVES
 DENSE  MEDAL
```

PUZZLE 160

```
BEL  CAUSE  HID
AGO  OTHER  EWE
TOWEROFLONDON
   ELAM  SOD
APRIL  SPINACH
FLEA  TAHOE  HI
TAD  BEGIN  OIL
EN  PANEL  DULL
RETURNS  RATES
   ANT  CULL
WALTERRALEIGH
IKE  ROUSE  VIE
GAS  STEER  EAR
```

PUZZLE 161

```
CAP  ADAPT  COW
AGO  WELSH  ABE
RAPHAEL  ELTON
  CARP  BAITED
FIORD  HOTLY
LORE  MONEY  SO
OWN  PIKER  VOX
PA  FILES  NILE
  ALLAY  CANON
IMPUGN  OOZE
SUPER  UPRIGHT
ILL  IBSEN  AIR
SEE  MEANY  REY
```

PUZZLE 162

```
HAT  ASTER  SHE
ACE  SHADE  CAW
STATION   STALE
    ADE  MIRROR
SHAPE   TODAY
LOTS  HONEY  MA
ABE  TOTES  FAN
TO  DELAY  CAST
   CAMEL  CORKS
STAMPS   COO
WORST  CARPETS
ART  ELOPE  LAP
YES  DATES  FRY
```

PUZZLE 163

```
LAP  SENDS  AGO
ELL  UTURN  IAN
GLEASON   EERIE
   ALAN  RAVENS
RISEN   POKED
ACES  HELEN  FT
RED  RIDER  ALI
ED  MIDAS  STAN
   MODEL  PATTY
SWORDS   BALE
PANEL  BESTMAN
ATE  EVENT  PRO
STY  SANTA  TED
```

PUZZLE 164

```
SWAT  SLIP  ATT
EIRE  LANA  THE
ENTERED   PARIS
    TOW  RECESS
STREW   FORCE
HOUR  BOAST  MD
ARM   AND   YOU
ME  MAIDS  BERT
   PASTA  FUNNY
SHIRTS   FAR
TENSE  BONNETS
ARE  REEL  EVIL
YES  SHED  DENY
```

"See you in the funny papers!"

PUZZLE 165

```
BAA  APART  PRO
ILL  LASER  LAD
TELLERS   AWARD
   ORE  SCENES
BEAST   WHERE
LACE  CHOSE  GA
AVE   AIR   FIG
BE  PRUNE  WAVE
   CLOSE  TIRED
PARADE   WON
ALONE  MADDENS
LAW  OPERA  YOU
END  SANDY  EWE
```

PUZZLE 166

```
AMID  HAWK  COP
BORE  IVAN  AVE
CROCODILE   LET
SENOR  ALLEARS
   RAPT   TAM
SAP  TIES  SITE
ELEVEN  MUTTER
ALTO  SPUR  YEN
   PIP  EGGS
HOEDOWN   EIGHT
APE  PIPEDREAM
LIV  ERAL  ERLE
LEE  SELL  NEON
```

PUZZLE 167

```
GAS  RAM  IOWA
AVERAGE   TWANG
GARAGE   FELINE
ICE  CAM  TAM
LEAK  JOT  PEP
ALL  MEN  BARON
WE  HATCHET  LO
SPRAY  EAT  BIT
HEM  PIT  MUSE
BAG  MAT  CAR
UNREAL  DOLLAR
STERN  POSTAGE
STAY  SET  POD
```

PUZZLE 168

```
        META
        ORAL
        TILL        POI
     SMOKEY      MARAT
DETER          AROSE
EWERS          GIST
WIRE          SIDES
NESS       EVA
GOTTERDAMMERUNG  ERMINE
     ENIGMA    SNEE
        DOE     ISNT
MARIO        OTTER
OMAR         MALTA
GRAVE     CREASE
EASES     HASH
ELS       ETTA
          TEAS
```

PUZZLE 169

```
FED  PLOP  SPED
ERA  AIDS  PALE
RIN  RED  POSSE
NEEDED   ROOT
   AD  COLLEGE
PAIN  RAVES  AL
ANN  WARES  ELL
IT  FACES  AREA
REMOVED   DI
   ARES  GARAGE
FARES  MUD  LAD
ODES  BOND  AVE
REST  ROSY  SEN
```

PUZZLE 170

```
R A T   A S T E R   P E A
O W E   S P A R E   L A G
W E A T H E R   T E A S E
    R E D   W I L T E D
C O L A S   H O R S E
A H O Y   P U R E E   P A
S I T   P U R R S   N I P
H O   T A R R Y   R O P E
    P A N S Y   A I D E S
S A L U T E   T S P
T R U T H   T I S S U E S
A I M   E L O P E   S A P
Y D S   R O O S T   E R A
```

PUZZLE 171

```
  D E G A S   E T H I C
D E D U C T   N O O D L E
I N   S T A I D   P E O N
V O W   A R B O R   A C T
O T I S   K I W I S   H E
T E N O R   S E T T L E R
    C U E D   D E A L
D R E S D E N   S T O L E
W E   A A R O N   E Y E D
A W E   N I M E S   D A W
R A R A   D E A T H   D I
F R I N G E   R E U B E N
  D E N I S   S T E I N
```

PUZZLE 172

```
P A S T   P R O M   I S M
A L O E   A U R A   B O A
D E S M O I N E S   I O N
      P A L   T A S T E
O F F E R   C H E F
D E A R   C O U R T E S Y
D A M   S H I N Y   D O E
S T E R L I N G   T E L L
    Y E N S   P A N E L
S H E E N   P A R
L A D   D E T E C T I V E
A I D   E R I E   A R I A
W R Y   R A N K   N E A R
```

PUZZLE 173

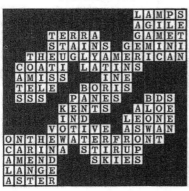

```
F A R   B L A M E   P E T
I C E   O I L E R   O D E
R E V E R S E   R I P E N
    V E T   R O D E N T
G R E E D   G I R L S
R O A R   T E N S E   W E
A P T   R E D   P A N
B E   G R A S S   B I N D
    S L I D E   S A N D S
B E H A V E   A P R
E L U D E   A R A B I A N
A L T   R U D E R   O W N
M A S   S P E A K   N E W
```

PUZZLE 174

```
C A B   B L A M E   S A D
O R E   R I D E R   T I E
D E T A I N S   A P E R S
    O D E   A S E A
S P I N E   B R E A K E R
H I K E   P E E R S   L O
A L E   B E T A S   S O W
D O   T O N E S   R I P E
E T E R N A L   W A T E R
    R E A L   M O P
S I R E N   P O R T A L S
A D O   Z E R O S   R I O
P A R   A L E R T   T E N
```

PUZZLE 175

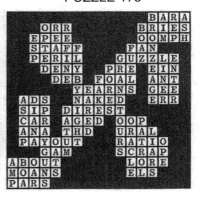

```
                  B A R A
    O R R       B R I E S
E P E E         O O M P H
S T A F F       F A N
P E R I L     G U Z Z L E
D E N Y   P R E     E I N
  D E B   F O A L   A N T
      Y E A R N S   G E E
                  E R R
A D S   N A K E D
S I P   D I R E S T
C A R   A G E D   O O P
A N A   T H D   U R A L
P A Y O U T   R A T I O
    G A M     S C R A P
A B O U T       L O R E
M O A N S       E L S
P A R S
```

PUZZLE 176

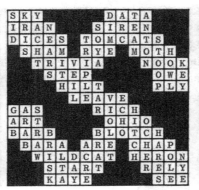

```
                  L A M P S
                  A G I L E
        T E R R A   G A M E T
      S T A I N S   G E M I N I
    T H E U G L Y A M E R I C A N
C O A T I   L A T I N S
A M I S S     I N E
T E L E   B O R I S
S S S   P A N E S   B D S
    K E N T S   A L O E
    I N D   L E O N E
    V O T I V E   A S W A N
O N T H E W A T E R F R O N T
C A R I N A   S T I R U P
A M E N D   S K I E S
L A N G E
A S T E R
```

PUZZLE 177

```
S K Y         D A T A
I R A N       S I R E N
D I C E S   T O M C A T S
S H A M   R Y E   M O T H
    T R I V I A   N O O K
      S T E P     O W E
      H I L T     P L Y
        L E A V E
G A S         R I C H
A R T         O H I O
B A R B   B L O T C H
B A R A   A R E   C H A P
  W I L D C A T   H E R O N
    S T A R T   R E L Y
    K A Y E     S E E
```

PUZZLE 178

```
        B O W
        L E N A
      A L A I N   M A R
      P R A D O   S I L O
  C A L M   N O   K N O B
H O S E A   R E A D E
T H E N   P E T T Y
S O O   H A G U E   C P A
    L A N A I   C H E W
    R E I G N   S H I N E
  D E E R   O Z   H U N T
  N A R Y   O P E R A
  A M Y   T R O L L
        A B E L
        P A T
```

PUZZLE 179

PUZZLE 180

PUZZLE 181

PUZZLE 182

PUZZLE 183

PUZZLE 184

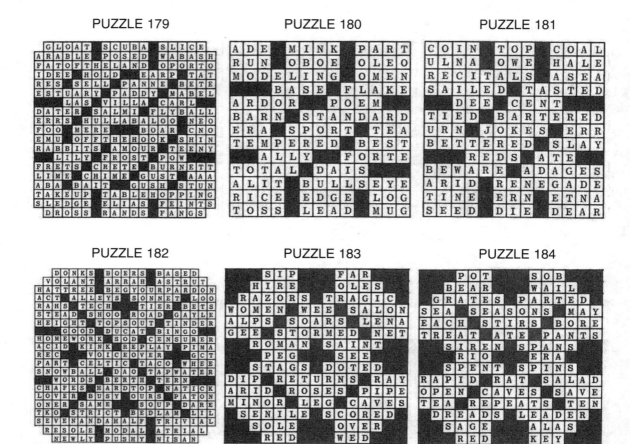

DIAGRAMLESS STARTING BOXES

124 Diagramless begins in the 7th box across
168 Diagramless begins in the 5th box across
175 Diagramless begins in the 14th box across
176 Diagramless begins in the 13th box across
177 Diagramless begins in the 1st box across
178 Diagramless begins in the 6th box across